COMMON CORE
ENGLISH
WORKBOOK

GRADE 8

prepaze

www.prepaze.com

Author: Ace Academic Publishing

Ace Academic Publishing is a leading supplemental educational workbook publisher for grades K-12. At Ace Academic Publishing, we realize the importance of imparting analytical and critical thinking skills during the early ages of childhood and hence our books include materials that require multiple levels of analysis and encourage the students to think outside the box.

The materials for our books are written by award winning teachers with several years of teaching experience. All our books are aligned with the state standards and are widely used by many schools throughout the country.

Prepaze is a sister company of Ace Academic Publishing. Intrigued by the unending possibilities of the internet and its role in education, Prepaze was created to spread the knowledge and learning across all corners of the world through an online platform. We equip ourselves with state-of-the-art technologies so that knowledge reaches the students through the quickest and the most effective channels.

For inquiries and bulk orders, contact Ace Academic Publishing at the following address:

Ace Academic Publishing
3736 Fallon Road #403
Dublin CA 94568

www.aceacademicpublishing.com

Ace Academic Publishing
ACHIEVING EXCELLENCE TOGETHER

ISBN: 978-1-949383-14-0

INTRODUCTION

About the Book

The content of the book includes multiple chapters and units covering all the required common core standards for the grade level. Similar to a standardized exam, you can find questions of all types — Multiple Choice, Fill in the blanks, True or False, Match the correct answer and Explain your Answers. The carefully chosen reading comprehension passages will help the students gain key comprehension skills such as themes, understanding figurative languages, character traits, and contextual vocabulary. The questions also cover writing standards that are not covered by most of the other commonly available workbooks. The exercises help students learn proper language convention and effectively use resources to research topics for writing essays. The detailed answer explanations help the students make sense of the problems and gain confidence in solving similar problems.

For the Parents

This workbook includes practice questions and tests that cover all the required Common Core Standards for the grade level. The book comprises multiple tests for each topic area so that your child can retake another test on the same topic. The workbook also includes questions for the writing standards and teaches your kid how to write essays and free responses. The workbook is divided into chapters and units so that you can choose the topics that you want your child to practice. The detailed answer explanations will teach your child the right methods to solve the problems for all types of questions, including the free-response questions. After completing the tests on all the chapters, your child can take any common core standardized exam with confidence and can excel in it.

For additional online practice, sign up for a free account at www.aceacademicprep.com.

For the Teachers

All questions and tests included in the Workbook are based on the core state standards and includes a clear label of the standard name. By following the chapter by chapter units, you can assign your students tests on a particular topic. The Workbook will help your students overcome any deficiencies in their understanding of critical concepts and will also help you identify the specific topics that may require more practice. The grade-appropriate, yet challenging questions will help your students learn to strategically use appropriate tools and persevere through common core standardized exams.

For additional online practice, sign up for a free account at www.aceacademicprep.com.

TABLE OF CONTENTS   GRADE 8

1. READING: LITERATURE

1. READING: LITERATURE

～～～ 1.1. Key Ideas and Details ～～～

Common Core State Standards: CCSS.ELA-LITERACY.RL.8.1, CCSS.ELA-LITERACY.RL.8.2, CCSS.ELA-LITERACY.RL.8.3

Skills:

- Cite textual evidence to support analysis of what the text says explicitly as well as inferences are drawn from the text.
- Determine a theme or central idea of a text and analyze its development over the course of the text.
- Provide an objective summary of the text.
- Analyze how particular lines of dialogue or incidents in a story or drama propel the action, reveal aspects of a character, or provoke a decision.

➢ *Directions: Read the passage and answer the questions below.*

=== **EXAMPLE** ===

> As the candidate for the mayoral race took the stand, the audience members murmured to one other. Peter Martin had just been caught embezzling money from his former employer and now he was entering the race to be the mayor. We couldn't believe it. He would be a politician, so he would be associating with his own kind.

E1   How does the audience most likely feel about Peter Martin? (RL.8.1)

   A. Honored and in awe
   B. Shocked and disappointed
   C. Amused and entertained
   D. Happy and enthusiastic

Answer: **B.** Based on context clues, the audience most likely feels shocked and disappointed.

prep⊙ze   Copyrighted Material   **www.prepaze.com**

1. READING: LITERATURE

=== EXAMPLE ===

Since all of the prominent citizens of the town would be at this function, my snooty neighbor believed that she would attend without a proper invitation. I suppressed my laughter whenever she mentioned her planned attendance at the Great Harwood Ball.

On the night of the event, my neighbor spent every waking minute trying to look perfect for the ball. Her formal gown obviously cost her an enormous amount of money. I peered through the window to see her make a dramatic walk to her rented limousine and off she went. I sat by the window waiting for her quick return once she was dismissed from the venue. However, to my utter surprise, my wait at the window would be quite a long one. My neighbor did not come back immediately. I spent hours upon hours staring down the street but to no avail. My tired eyes forced me to go to bed.

The next morning, the local news channel covered the ball, as it was the biggest news story of the day. I watched intensely to rub it into my neighbor's face how I failed to see her presence from the extensive news coverage of the event. Surprisingly, as the cameraman panned around the ballroom, he focused on my neighbor who was mingling with the rich aristocrats.

E2 **How does the narrator's point of view about her neighbor contribute to the central idea of the story?** (RL.8.2)

A. She sees the neighbor's attitude as one of excessive confidence and pride.

B. She sees the neighbor's attitude as one of jealousy and arrogance

C. She sees the neighbor's attitude as one of humor and playfulness.

D. The neighbor's attitude does not contribute to the overall theme.

Answer: **A.** Based on context clues, the narrator views the neighbor's actions as overly confident and prideful.

  prepaze

1. READING: LITERATURE

================ **EXAMPLE** ================

LORD OF THE FLIES

The space under the palm trees was full of noise and movement. Ralph was on his feet too, shouting for quiet, but no one heard him. All at once the crowd swayed toward the island and was gone—following Jack. Even the tiny children went and did their best among the leaves and broken branches. Ralph was left, holding the conch, with no one but Piggy.

Piggy's breathing was quite restored.

"Like kids! He said scornfully. "Acting like a crowd of kids!"

Ralph looked at him doubtfully and laid the conch on the tree trunk. "I bet it's gone tea-time," said Piggy. "What do they think they're going to do on that mountain?"

E3 **Which phrase from the text reveals Piggy's feelings towards the other characters?** (RL.8.3)

A. "Like kids! He said scornfully. "Acting like a crowd of kids!"

B. "I bet it's gone tea-time," said Piggy.

C. The space under the palm trees was full of noise and movement.

D. Ralph looked at him doubtfully and laid the conch on the tree trunk.

Answer: **A.** The dialogue reveals that Piggy believes their behavior is childish. Also, the narrator describes Piggy's tone as scornful.

1. READING: LITERATURE

> *Directions: Read the passage and answer the questions below.*

GREAT EXPECTATIONS

This was very uncomfortable, and I was half afraid. However, the only thing to be done being to knock at the door, I knocked, and was told from within to enter. I entered, therefore, and found myself in a pretty large room, well lighted with wax candles. No glimpse of daylight was to be seen in it. It was a dressing-room, as I supposed from the furniture, though much of it was of forms and uses then quite unknown to me. But prominent in it was a draped table with a gilded looking-glass, and that I made out at first sight to be a fine lady's dressing-table.

Whether I should have made out this object so soon, if there had been no lady sitting at it, I cannot say. In an arm-chair, with an elbow resting on the table and her head leaning on that hand, sat the strangest lady I have ever seen, or shall ever see.

She was dressed in rich materials - satins, and lace, and silks - all of white. Her shoes were white. And she had a long white veil dependent from her hair, and she had bridal flowers in her hair, but her hair was white. Some bright jewels sparkled on her neck and on her hands, and some other jewels lay sparkling on the table. Dresses, less splendid than the dress she wore, and half-packed trunks, were scattered about. She had not quite finished dressing, for she had but one shoe on - the other was on the table near her hand - her veil was but half arranged, her watch and chain were not put on, and with her handkerchief, and gloves, and some flowers, and a prayer-book, all confusedly heaped about the looking-glass.

It was not in the first few moments that I saw all these things, though I saw more of them in the first moments than might be supposed. But, I saw that everything within my view which ought to be white, had been white long ago, and had lost its lustre, and was faded and yellow. I saw that the bride within the bridal dress had withered like the dress, and like the flowers, and had no brightness left but the brightness of her sunken eyes. I saw that the dress had been put upon the rounded figure of a young woman,

...continued next page

1. READING: LITERATURE

and that the figure upon which it now hung loose, had shrunk to skin and bone. Once, I had been taken to see some ghastly waxwork at the Fair, representing I know not what impossible personage lying in state. Once, I had been taken to one of our old marsh churches to see a skeleton in the ashes of a rich dress, that had been dug out of a vault under the church pavement. Now, waxwork and skeleton seemed to have dark eyes that moved and looked at me. I should have cried out, if I could.

MULTIPLE CHOICE

1.1. KEY IDEAS AND DETAILS

1. **What can the reader infer from this sentence:** (RL.8.1)

    "She had a long white veil dependent from her hair, and she had bridal flowers in her hair, but her hair was white."

    A. The narrator thinks that it is strange for someone old to be dressed as a bride.
    B. The woman's veil made her hair difficult to see.
    C. The narrator doesn't like the woman's hair.
    D. The flowers in the woman's hair belonged to the narrator.

2. **What does the narrator conclude about the woman's clothing and materials?** (RL.8.1)

    A. They are wedding gifts.
    B. They are old and run-down.
    C. She doesn't want them anymore.
    D. They do not belong to her.

3. **According to this passage, what can you infer about the narrator?** (RL.8.1)

    A. He is uncomfortable and even frightened in this house.
    B. He knows the woman personally and feels let down.
    C. He is a dress designer who is shocked at the conditions.
    D. He is enjoying his time at the woman's house and expects a party.

1. READING: LITERATURE

> *Directions: Read the passage and answer the questions below.*

GREAT EXPECTATIONS

"Who is it?" said the lady at the table.

"Pip, ma'am."

"Pip?"

"Mr. Pumblechook's boy, ma'am. Come – to play."

"Come nearer; let me look at you. Come close."

It was when I stood before her, avoiding her eyes, that I took note of the surrounding objects in detail, and saw that her watch had stopped at twenty minutes to nine, and that a clock in the room had stopped at twenty minutes to nine.

"Look at me," said Miss Havisham. "You are not afraid of a woman who has never seen the sun since you were born?"

I regret to state that I was not afraid of telling the enormous lie comprehended in the answer "No."

"Do you know what I touch here?" she said, laying her hands, one upon the other, on her left side.

"Yes, ma'am." (It made me think of the young man.)

"What do I touch?"

"Your heart."

"Broken!"

She uttered the word with an eager look, and with strong emphasis, and with a weird smile that had a kind of boast in it. Afterwards, she kept her hands there for a little while, and slowly took them away as if they were heavy.

=== FILL IN THE BLANK ===

4. According to the text, the clocks in the room are stopped
to _____. (RL.8.1)

5. The woman describes her _____ as broken in the text. (RL.8.1)

Copyrighted Material prepaze

1. READING: LITERATURE

== **MULTIPLE CHOICE** ==

6. **Pip's response to Miss Havisham's question, "You are not afraid of a woman who has never seen the sun since you were born?" most likely implies that:** (RL.8.1)

   A. He is confused about his answer.

   B. He is not being honest and is afraid.

   C. He is honestly not afraid of the woman.

   D. He does not respond to the woman's question.

> ➤ *Directions: Read the passage and answer the questions below.*

1.1. KEY IDEAS AND DETAILS

GIFT OF THE MAGI

Jim stopped inside the door, as immovable as a setter at the scent of quail. His eyes were fixed upon Della, and there was an expression in them that she could not read, and it terrified her. It was not anger, nor surprise, nor disapproval, nor horror, nor any of the sentiments that she had been prepared for. He simply stared at her fixedly with that peculiar expression on his face.

Della wriggled off the table and went for him.

"Jim," she cried, "don't look at me that way. I had my hair cut off and sold because I couldn't have lived through Christmas without giving you a present. It'll grow out again—you won't mind, will you? I just had to do it. My hair grows awfully fast. Say 'Merry Christmas!' Jim, and let's be happy. You don't know what a nice—what a beautiful, nice gift I've got for you."

"You've cut off your hair?" asked Jim, laboriously, as if he had not arrived at that patent fact yet even after the hardest mental labor.

"Cut it off and sold it," said Della. " I'm me without my hair, aren't I?"

Jim looked about the room curiously.

1. READING: LITERATURE

7. According to the text, what did Della do to her hair? (RL.8.1)

 A. She cut and sold it to pay for Jim's present.
 B. She cut it because she wanted a new hairstyle.
 C. She cut it herself because she couldn't afford the salon.
 D. She cut it order to surprise Jim with a new, attractive look.

8. Which word best describes Jim's reaction to Della's hair? (RL.8.1)

 A. Disgust   **B.** Glee   **C.** Intrigued   **D.** Horror

> ➤ *Directions: Read the passage and answer the questions below.*

1.1. KEY IDEAS AND DETAILS

THE FOX AND THE HORSE

 A peasant had a faithful horse which had grown old and could do no more work, so his master no longer wanted to give him anything to eat and said, "I can certainly make no more use of you, but still I mean well by you, and if you prove yourself still strong enough to bring me a lion here, I will maintain you. But for now get out of my stable." And with that he chased him into the open field.

 The horse was sad, and went to the forest to seek a little protection there from the weather. There the fox met him and said, "Why do you hang your head so, and go about all alone?"

 "Alas," replied the horse, "greed and loyalty do not dwell together in one house. My master has forgotten what services I have performed for him for so many years, and because I can no longer plow well, he will give me no more food, and has driven me out."

 "Without giving you a chance?" asked the fox.

 "The chance was a bad one. He said, if I were still strong enough to bring him a lion, he would keep me, but he well knows that I cannot do that."

 The fox said, "I will help you. Just lie down, stretch out as if you were dead, and do not stir."

...continued next page

1. READING: LITERATURE

The horse did what the fox asked, and then the fox went to the lion, who had his den not far off, and said, "A dead horse is lying out there. Just come with me, and you can have a rich meal."

The lion went with him, and when they were both standing by the horse the fox said, "After all, it is not very comfortable for you here -- I tell you what -- I will fasten it to you by the tail, and then you can drag it into your cave and eat it in peace."

This advice pleased the lion. He positioned himself, and in order that the fox might tie the horse fast to him, he kept completely quiet. But the fox tied the lion's legs together with the horse's tail, and twisted and fastened everything so well and so strongly that no amount of strength could pull it loose. When he had finished his work, he tapped the horse on the shoulder and said, "Pull, white horse, pull!"

Then up sprang the horse at once, and pulled the lion away with him. The lion began to roar so that all the birds in the forest flew up in terror, but the horse let him roar, and drew him and dragged him across the field to his master's door. When the master saw the lion, he was of a better mind, and said to the horse, "You shall stay with me and fare well." And he gave him plenty to eat until he died.

MULTIPLE CHOICE

9. One possible theme of this story could be: (RL.8.2)
- **A.** Never betray a loyal friend.
- **B.** Cleverness can overcome ferocity.
- **C.** Big creatures are wiser than small ones.
- **D.** Always trust those who are cunning.

10. Which of the following is a supporting theme of the story? (RL.8.2)
- **A.** It is important to be a good worker.
- **B.** Servants should not disobey their masters.
- **C.** Foxes are extremely cunning animals.
- **D.** Teamwork can make a difficult task possible.

1. READING: LITERATURE

11. **How does the master change from the beginning of the story to the end?** (RL.8.2)

A. He changes from loving his horse to being upset with it.

B. The master compares himself to his old horse, realizing he is old too.

C. He changes from discarding his faithful horse to caring for him forever.

D. He first believes that the horse is skillful, but then realizes it is lazy.

═══════════════ **FREE RESPONSE** ═══════════════

12. **Write a summary of the passage.** (RL.8.2)

_____

_____

_____

_____

_____

_____

_____

_____

_____

_____

_____

1.1. KEY IDEAS AND DETAILS

1. READING: LITERATURE

_____

_____

_____

_____

_____

_____

_____

> ➢ *Directions: Read the passage and answer the questions below.*

THE DAISY

Now listen! In the country, close by the high road, stood a farm-house; perhaps you have passed by and seen it yourself. There was a little flower garden with painted wooden palings in front of it; close by was a ditch, on its fresh green bank grew a little daisy; the sun shone as warmly and brightly upon it as on the magnificent garden flowers, and therefore it thrived well. One morning it had quite opened, and its little snow-white petals stood round the yellow centre, like the rays of the sun. It did not mind that nobody saw it in the grass, and that it was a poor despised flower; on the contrary, it was quite happy, and turned towards the sun, looking upward and listening to the song of the lark high up in the air.

The little daisy was as happy as if the day had been a great holi-day, but it was only Monday. All the children were at school, and while they were sitting on the forms and learning their lessons, it sat on its thin green stalk and learnt from the sun and from its surroundings how kind God is, and it rejoiced that the song of the little lark expressed so sweetly and distinctly its own feelings. With a sort of reverence the daisy looked up to the bird that could fly and sing, but it did not feel envious. "I can see and hear," it thought; "the sun shines upon me, and the forest kisses me. How rich I am!"

...continued next page

 www.prepaze.com

1. READING: LITERATURE

In the garden close by grew many large and magnificent flowers, and, strange to say, the less fragrance they had the haughtier and prouder they were. The peonies puffed themselves up in order to be larger than the roses, but size is not everything! The tulips had the finest colours, and they knew it well, too, for they were standing bolt upright like candles, that one might see them the better. In their pride they did not see the little daisy, which looked over to them and thought, "How rich and beautiful they are! I am sure the pretty bird will fly down and call upon them. Thank God, that I stand so near and can at least see all the splendour." And while the daisy was still thinking, the lark came flying down, crying "Tweet," but not to the peonies and tulips—no, into the grass to the poor daisy. Its joy was so great that it did not know what to think. The little bird hopped round it and sang, "How beautifully soft the grass is, and what a lovely little flower with its golden heart and silver dress is growing here." The yellow centre in the daisy did indeed look like gold, while the little petals shone as brightly as silver.

How happy the daisy was! No one has the least idea. The bird kissed it with its beak, sang to it, and then rose again up to the blue sky. It was certainly more than a quarter of an hour before the daisy recovered its senses. Half ashamed, yet glad at heart, it looked over to the other flowers in the garden; surely they had witnessed its pleasure and the honour that had been done to it; they understood its joy. But the tulips stood more stiffly than ever, their faces were pointed and red, because they were vexed. The peonies were sulky; it was well that they could not speak, otherwise they would have given the daisy a good lecture. The little flower could very well see that they were ill at ease, and pitied them sincerely.

 prepaze

1. READING: LITERATURE

=== **MULTIPLE CHOICE** ===

13. **How does the author's description of the flowers at the beginning of the story contribute to the theme?** (RL.8.2)

  A. The layout of the flowers sets the scene for the main character's attitude and behavior.

  B. It allows the reader to visualize where each event will take place in the story.

  C. This foreshadows the major problem that will take place later in the story.

  D. It presents a vivid image at the beginning of the story.

14. **How does the communication between the bird and the daisy develop the theme?** (RL.8.2)

  A. Their interactions create a sense of joy and camaraderie.

  B. Their collaboration of ideas effectively resolved the problem for them.

  C. Communication between the bird and daisy lessened their bond.

  D. Due to their interactions, they end up creating the problem in the story.

> ➤ *Directions: Read the passage and answer the questions below*

OLIVER TWIST

   The room in which the boys were fed, was a large stone hall, with a copper at one end: out of which the master, dressed in an apron for the purpose, and assisted by one or two women, ladled the gruel at meal-times.

   Of this festive composition each boy had one porringer[1], and no more- except on occasions of great public rejoicing, when he had two ounces and a quarter of bread besides. The bowls never wanted washing. The boys polished them with their spoons till they shone again; and when they had performed this operation (which never

...continued next page

---

1   A small bowl used for soup or stew

1. READING: LITERATURE

took very long, the spoons being nearly as large as the bowls), they would sit staring at the copper, with such eager eyes, as if they could have devoured the very bricks of which it was composed; employing themselves, meanwhile, in sucking their fingers most assiduously[2], with the view of catching up any stray splashes of gruel that might have been cast thereon. Boys have generally excellent appetites. Oliver Twist and his companions suffered the tortures of slow starvation for three months: at last they got so voracious and wild with hunger, that one boy, who was tall for his age, and hadn't been used to that sort of thing (for his father had kept a small cookshop), hinted darkly to his companions, that unless he had another basin of gruel per diem[3], he was afraid he might some night happen to eat the boy who slept next him, who happened to be a weakly youth of tender age. He had a wild, hungry eye; and they implicitly believed him. A council was held; lots were cast who should walk up to the master after supper that evening, and ask for more; and it fell to Oliver Twist.

The evening arrived; the boys took their places. The master, in his cook's uniform, stationed himself at the copper; his pauper assistants ranged themselves behind him; the gruel was served out; and a long grace was said over the short commons. The gruel disappeared; the boys whispered each other, and winked at Oliver; while his next neighbours nudged him. Child as he was, he was desperate with hunger, and reckless with misery. He rose from the table; and advancing to the master, basin and spoon in hand, said: somewhat alarmed at his own temerity[4]:

"Please, sir, I want some more."

MULTIPLE CHOICE

15. **Why is Oliver the only boy to ask for more food?** (RL.8.3)

   A. He is singled out by the men in charge.

   B. The other boys prompted Oliver to ask for more food.

   C. Oliver is hungrier than the other boys.

   D. Oliver is threatened and bullied by the other boys.

---

2   With great care and persistence
3   Daily
4   Confidence or boldness

1. READING: LITERATURE

16. **Which line from the text best describes why Oliver asks for more food?** (RL.8.3)

   A. The bowls never wanted washing. The boys polished them with their spoons till they shone again...

   B. Oliver Twist and his companions suffered the tortures of slow starvation for three months...

   C. A council was held; lots were cast who should walk up to the master after supper that evening, and ask for more; and it fell to Oliver Twist.

   D. The master, in his cook's uniform, stationed himself at the copper.

> ➤ *Directions: Read the passage and answer the questions below*

1.1. KEY IDEAS AND DETAILS

OLIVER TWIST

The master was a fat, healthy man; but he turned very pale. He gazed in astonishment on the small rebel for some seconds, and then clung for support to the copper. The assistants were paralyzed with wonder; the boys with fear.

"What!" said the master at length, in a faint voice.

"Please, sir," replied Oliver, "I want some more."

The board were sitting in solemn conclave, when Mr. Bumble rushed into the room in great excitement, and addressing the gentleman in the high chair, said, "Mr. Limbkins, I beg your pardon, sir! Oliver Twist has asked for more!"

There was a general start. Horror was depicted on every countenance.

"For more!" said Mr. Limbkins. "Compose yourself, Bumble, and answer me distinctly. Do I understand that he asked for more, after he had eaten the supper allotted by the dietary?"

"He did, sir," replied Bumble.

1. READING: LITERATURE

=== **MULTIPLE CHOICE** ===

17. What is the result of Oliver's request for more food? (RL.8.3)

A. The other boys demand that they also get more food.

B. He is rewarded for his bravery.

C. He is reported to Mr. Limbkins.

D. He receives more food.

18. What does this dialogue from the text reveal? (RL.8.3)

"What!" said the master at length, in a faint voice,"

A. The master believes that Oliver is confused.

B. The master is weak and unable to say no to Oliver.

C. The master is shocked and insulted that anyone would ask for more food.

D. The master is unable to contain his excitement over Oliver's request.

> *Directions: Read the passage and answer the questions below.*

RAPUNZEL

Rapunzel grew into the most beautiful child under the sun. When she was twelve years old, the enchantress shut her into a tower, which lay in a forest, and had neither stairs nor door, but quite at the top was a little window. When the enchantress wanted to go in, she placed herself beneath it and cried:

"Rapunzel, Rapunzel,

Let down your hair to me."

Rapunzel had magnificent long hair, fine as spun gold, and when she heard the voice of the enchantress she unfastened her braided tresses, wound them round one of the hooks of the window above, and then the hair fell twenty ells down, and the enchantress climbed up by it.

After a year or two, it came to pass that the king's son rode through the forest and passed by the tower. Then he heard a song, which was

...continued next page

1.1. KEY IDEAS AND DETAILS

 prepaze

1. READING: LITERATURE

so charming that he stood still and listened. This was Rapunzel, who in her solitude passed her time in letting her sweet voice resound. The king's son wanted to climb up to her, and looked for the door of the tower, but none was to be found. He rode home, but the singing had so deeply touched his heart, that every day he went out into the forest and listened to it. Once when he was thus standing behind a tree, he saw that an enchantress came there, and he heard how she cried:

"Rapunzel, Rapunzel,

Let down your hair to me."

Then Rapunzel let down the braids of her hair, and the enchantress climbed up to her. "If that is the ladder by which one mounts, I too will try my fortune," said he, and the next day when it began to grow dark, he went to the tower and cried:

"Rapunzel, Rapunzel,

Let down your hair to me."

Immediately the hair fell down and the king's son climbed up.

═══ MULTIPLE CHOICE ═══

19. **How does Rapunzel's singing impact the action of the story?** (RL.8.3)

   A. It draws the king's son to her.

   B. It causes the enchantress to lock Rapunzel in the tower.

   C. It allows her to escape from the tower.

   D. It makes her happy to sing.

20. **Why is the following line repeated in the story?** (RL.8.3)

   "Rapunzel, Rapunzel,
   Let down your hair to me."

   A. This line emphasizes the significance of Rapunzel's hair.

   B. This line signals a flashback when it appears in the story.

   C. The author mistakenly reprinted this line.

   D. This line only appears once in the story.

1.2. CRAFT AND STRUCTURE ▷▷▷

prepaze

www.prepaze.com

1. READING: LITERATURE

1.2. Craft and Structure

Common Core State Standards: CCSS.ELA-LITERACY.RL.8.5, CCSS.ELA-LITERACY.RL.8.6

Skills:
- Compare and contrast text structure.
- Analyze differences in points of view (character, audience, etc.).

> ➤ *Directions: Read each poem and answer the questions below.*

=== **EXAMPLE** ===

POEM 1

Stars twinkle brightly in the midnight sky

Birds chirp loudly and soar up high

Clouds glide softly in the air nearby

I gaze at these wonders with a curious eye

I long to know who painted the sky

POEM 2

The frigid wind whisked past his cheek

His feet sank into the freezing snow

He wrestled against the bitter cold

He had faith that he would make it home

E1 **How are these poems similar in structure and/or style?** (RL.8.5)

    A. They are both chronological texts.

    B. They both present a problem and suggest a solution.

    C. They are both written in a descriptive style.

    D. They both compare and contrast two or more subjects.

Answer: **C.** A descriptive text uses sensory language to set a specific tone. Both poems are written in a descriptive style.

prepaze

1. READING: LITERATURE

=== EXAMPLE ===

THE TELL-TALE HEART

It is impossible to say how first the idea entered my brain; but once conceived, it haunted me day and night. Object there was none. Passion there was none. I loved the old man. He had never wronged me. He had never given me insult. For his gold I had no desire. I think it was his eye! yes, it was this! One of his eyes resembled that of a vulture—a pale blue eye, with a film over it.

E2 **How does the narrator describe his feelings towards the old man?** (RL.8.6)

A. He expresses his hatred and envy towards the old man.

B. He believes that the old man constantly mistreated him.

C. His expressive his pity for the old man.

D. His expresses his affection towards the old man.

Answer: **D.** The narrator states, " I loved the old man. He had never wronged me." This conveys his affection towards the old man.

> ➤ *Directions: Read each passage and answer the questions below.*

PASSAGE 1

Yesterday, I baked a cake with my grandpa. The instructions were very simple. First, I turned the oven on. Next, we gathered the dry ingredients. We needed flour, sugar and salt. We also used wet ingredients such as eggs, oil and milk. Grandpa mixed all everything together and poured the batter into a pan. After we put the cake into the oven, we let it bake for 30 minutes. Lastly, we put chocolate frosting on the cake. It was delicious!

PASSAGE 2

Manuel and his grandpa were mesmerized by the fragrant smell of pastries. They gazed at the display of sweets in the bakery window. "I want that one," said Manuel as he pointed to a shiny, glazed cake. It was topped with shimmering sugar sprinkles.

...continued next page

1. READING: LITERATURE

Grandpa replied, "That would be perfect for the party!"

The baker greeted them as they walked inside. "Hello. What would you like today?" Manuel was tempted by all the pleasant sights and scents, but his heart was set on the sparkly cake.

Grandpa said, "We would like that pretty cake in the window."

The baker grinned widely as she answered, "Great choice. That cake is my favorite, too. I'll pack it up for you right now." Manuel was ecstatic as he walked out the door with the cake box. He had found the perfect cake for his grandma's surprise party.

MULTIPLE CHOICE

1. **Which best describes the text structure seen in Passage 1?** (RL.8.5)
   A. Cause and effect
   B. Chronological
   C. Compare and contrast
   D. Problem and solution

2. **Which sentence helps to identify the text structure in Passage 1?** (RL.8.5)
   A. Yesterday, I baked a cake with my grandpa.
   B. The instructions were very simple.
   C. First, I turned the oven on.
   D. We also used wet ingredients like eggs, oil and milk.

3. **Which best describes the text structure seen in Passage 2?** (RL.8.5)
   A. Chronological
   B. Compare and contrast
   C. Descriptive
   D. Cause and effect

4. **Which sentence helps to identify the text structure in Passage 2?** (RL.8.5)
   A. Grandpa replied, "That would be perfect for the party!"
   B. That cake is my favorite too.
   C. The baker greeted them as they walked inside.
   D. Manuel and his grandpa were mesmerized by the fragrant smell of pastries.

1. READING: LITERATURE

5. **What is the main difference between the two passages?** (RL.8.5)
    A. Passage 1 lists a sequence of events; Passage 2 tells a story.
    B. Passage 1 is based on facts; Passage 2 is based on an opinion.
    C. Passage 1 explores cause and effect; Passage 2 lists a sequence of events.
    D. Passage 1 compares two subjects; Passage 2 contrasts two subjects.

➤ *Directions: Read each passage and answer the questions below.*

PASSAGE 1

There are hundreds of dog breeds all over the world. Each breed of dogs has its own set of characteristics. Dogs will differ in appearance, personality, and function based on their breeds. For example, some dogs are considered to be companion dogs while others are good for hunting. Dogs such as Great Danes and Scottish Deerhounds are very large. Chihuahuas and Yorkshire Terriers, on the other hand, are small, lightweight dogs. Dogs also have a wide range of temperaments. Some dogs are affectionate and gentle, which makes them good domestic pets. Wild, vicious dogs are not recommended to live in homes. Dog breed research makes it easy to identify the features and roles of specific dogs.

PASSAGE 2

My dog is my favorite pet. I have a cat and a hamster too, but my dog is the best. Dogs are better than other pets because they like to play games. I tried to toss a Frisbee to my cat, but she could not catch it. I took my hamster for a walk but he just stood still. That is why dogs are better. Also, dogs love to take baths. My cat detests water! My poor hamster panicked and almost drowned. Another reason why I love dogs is because they are extremely friendly. My hamster is adorable, but he doesn't like hugs. My cat is very keen, but she won't do any tricks for me. Unlike other pets, dogs are playful, courageous and affectionate. That is why dogs are the best pets in the world.

prepaze   **www.prepaze.com**

1. READING: LITERATURE

=== MULTIPLE CHOICE ===

6. **Which of the following best describes the text structure seen in Passage 1?**
   - **A.** Cause and effect
   - **B.** Sequence of events
   - **C.** Compare and contrast
   - **D.** Problem and solution

7. **Which of the following best describes the text structure seen in Passage 2?**
   - **A.** Chronological
   - **B.** Compare and contrast
   - **C.** Descriptive
   - **D.** Cause and effect

8. **Which of the following best describes the style in which Passage 1 is written?**
   - **A.** Persuasive
   - **B.** Narrative
   - **C.** Chronological
   - **D.** Expository

9. **Which of the following best describes the style in which Passage 2 is written?**
   - **A.** Persuasive   **B.** Sequential   **C.** Informative   **D.** Expository

10. **How are these passages similar in structure and/or style?**
    - **A.** They both list a sequence of events.
    - **B.** They are both written in a narrative style.
    - **C.** They both compare and contrast two or more subjects.
    - **D.** They both present a problem and suggest a solution.

11. **What is the main difference between the two passages?**
    - **A.** Passage 1 presents a problem; Passage 2 presents a solution.
    - **B.** Passage 1 is based on facts; Passage 2 is based on an opinion.
    - **C.** Passage 1 is written in a narrative style; Passage 2 is written in an expository style.
    - **D.** Passage 1 is a fictional text; Passage 2 is non-fiction.

1.2. CRAFT AND STRUCTURE

1. READING: LITERATURE

> ➤ *Directions:* *Read the passage and answer the questions below.*

BLACK BEAUTY: THE AUTOBIOGRAPHY OF A HORSE

When I was four years old Squire Gordon came to look at me. He examined my eyes, my mouth, and my legs; he felt them all down; and then I had to walk and trot and gallop before him. He seemed to like me, and said, "When he has been well broken in he will do very well." My master said he would break me in himself, as he should not like me to be frightened or hurt, and he lost no time about it, for the next day he began.

Every one may not know what breaking in is, therefore I will describe it. It means to teach a horse to wear a saddle and bridle, and to carry on his back a man, woman or child; to go just the way they wish, and to go quietly. Besides this he has to learn to wear a collar, a crupper, and a breeching, and to stand still while they are put on; then to have a cart or chaise fixed behind, so that he cannot walk or trot without dragging it after him; and he must go fast or slow, just as his driver wishes. He must never start at what he sees, nor speak to other horses, nor bite, nor kick, nor have any will of his own; but always do his master's will, even though he may be very tired or hungry; but the worst of all is, when his harness is once on, he may neither jump for joy nor lie down for weariness. So you see this breaking in is a great thing.

I had of course been used to a halter and a headstall, and to be led about in the fields and lanes quietly, but now I was to have a bit and bridle; my master gave me some oats as usual, and after a good deal of coaxing he got the bit into my mouth, and the bridle fixed, but it was a nasty thing! Those who have never had a bit in their mouths cannot think how bad it feels; a great piece of cold hard steel as thick as a man's finger to be pushed into one's mouth, between one's teeth, and over one's tongue, with the ends coming out at the corner of your mouth, and held fast there by straps over your head, under your throat, round your nose, and under your chin; so that no way in the world can you get rid of the nasty hard thing; it is very bad! Yes, very bad! At least I thought so; but I knew my mother always wore one when she went out, and all horses did when they were grown up; and so, what with the nice oats, and what with my master's pats, kind words, and gentle ways, I got to wear my bit and bridle.

...continued next page

1. READING: LITERATURE

Next came the saddle, but that was not half so bad; my master put it on my back very gently, while old Daniel held my head; he then made the girths fast under my body, patting and talking to me all the time; then I had a few oats, then a little leading about; and this he did every day till I began to look for the oats and the saddle. At length, one morning, my master got on my back and rode me round the meadow on the soft grass.

MULTIPLE CHOICE

12. **The narrator in the story is** _____. (RL.8.6)

   A. The master
   B. The horse
   C. Squire Gordon
   D. A narrator outside of the story

13. **The story is narrated from the** _____ **point of view.** (RL.8.6)

   A. First person
   B. Second person
   C. Third person
   D. Limited omniscient

14. **How does the narrator feel about the breaking in process?** (RL.8.6)

   A. It is a joyful experience for the horse.
   B. It is beneficial for the horse to be in control.
   C. It is uncomfortable for the horse.
   D. It is necessary in order for a horse to be civilized.

15. **Which line from the text reveals the narrator's point of view about "breaking in?"** (RL.8.6)

   A. "It means to teach a horse to wear a saddle and bridle, and to carry on his back a man, woman or child…"
   B. "…and he must go fast or slow, just as his driver wishes."
   C. "So you see this breaking in is a great thing."
   D. "Those who have never had a bit in their mouths cannot think how bad it feels…"

 prepaze

1. READING: LITERATURE

16. **Which statement best describes the horse's master's point of view about "breaking in?"**

A. He explains that the horse must be broken in or he will sell it.

B. He realizes the process is uncomfortable for the horse and tries to be tender.

C. He believes that breaking in should be done as harshly as possible.

D. He thinks that it is too difficult for a master to break in a horse.

> ➤ *Directions: Read the poem and answer the questions below.*

MENDING WALL

One on a side. It comes to little more:

There where it is we do not need the wall:

He is all pine and I am apple orchard.

My apple trees will never get across

And eat the cones under his pines, I tell him.

He only says, "Good fences make good neighbors."

Spring is the mischief in me, and I wonder

If I could put a notion in his head:

"Why do they make good neighbors? Isn't it

Where there are cows? But here there are no cows.

Before I built a wall I'd ask to know

What I was walling in or walling out,

And to whom I was like to give offence.

Something there is that doesn't love a wall,

That wants it down."

1. READING: LITERATURE

=== **MULTIPLE CHOICE** ===

17. **Which statement best describes the conflicting views in this poem?** (RL.8.6)

    A. The author does not like pine trees, but his neighbor does.

    B. The author does not want a fence between them, but his neighbor does.

    C. The author wants to have cows, but his neighbor does not.

    D. Neither the author nor his neighbor wants a fence between them.

18. **Which of these lines best reveal the conflicting views in this poem?** (RL.8.6)

    A. He is all pine and I am apple orchard; My apple trees will never get across and eat the cones under his pines, I tell him.

    B. Before I built a wall I'd ask to know; What I was walling in or walling out

    C. There where it is we do not need the wall; He only says, "Good fences make good neighbors."

    D. Spring is the mischief in me, and I wonder; Where there are cows? But here there are no cows.

19. **What does this line reveal about the conflicting views in this poem?** (RL.8.6)

    If I could put a notion in his head

    A. The author wants to change his neighbor's mind.

    B. The author wants to put a thing on his neighbor's head.

    C. The author wants to hypnotize his neighbor.

    D. The author wants to know what his neighbor is thinking.

20. **How does the neighbors' conflict affect the tone of the poem?** (RL.8.6)

    A. It creates a sense of comedy and fun.

    B. It creates a sense of rivalry and tension.

    C. It creates a sense of mystery and darkness.

    D. It creates a sense of shock and suspense.

1.3. INTEGRATION OF KNOWLEDGE AND IDEAS

1.2. CRAFT AND STRUCTURE

1. READING: LITERATURE

~~ 1.3. Integration of Knowledge and Ideas ~~

Common Core State Standards: CCSS.ELA-LITERACY.RL.8.9

Skills:
- Compare and contrast fictional and traditional texts.
- Analyze themes, patterns of events, and characters.

> ➤ *Directions: Read the passages and answer the questions below.*

=== **EXAMPLE** ===

GIFT OF THE MAGI

Jim had not yet seen his beautiful present. She held it out to him eagerly upon her open palm. The dull precious metal seemed to flash with a reflection of her bright and ardent spirit.

"Isn't it a dandy, Jim? I hunted all over town to find it. You'll have to look at the time a hundred times a day now. Give me your watch. I want to see how it looks on it."

Instead of obeying, Jim tumbled down on the couch and put his hands under the back of his head and smiled.

"Dell," said he, "let's put our Christmas presents away and keep 'em a while. They're too nice to use just at present. I sold the watch to get the money to buy your combs. And now suppose you put the chops on."

The magi, as you know, were wise men—wonderfully wise men—who brought gifts to the Babe in the manger. They invented the art of giving Christmas presents. Being wise, their gifts were no doubt wise ones, possibly bearing the privilege of exchange in case of duplication. And here I have lamely related to you the uneventful chronicle of two foolish children in a flat who most unwisely sacrificed for each other the greatest treasures of their house. But in a last word to the wise of these days let it be said that of all who give gifts these two were the wisest. Of all who give and receive gifts, such as they are wisest. Everywhere they are wisest. They are the magi.

...continued next page

1. READING: LITERATURE

THE GOSPEL OF MATTHEW

Then Herod called the Magi secretly and found out from them the exact time the star had appeared.

He sent them to Bethlehem and said, "Go and search carefully for the child. As soon as you find him, report to me, so that I too may go and worship him."

After they had heard the king, they went on their way, and the star they had seen when it rose went ahead of them until it stopped over the place where the child was.

When they saw the star, they were overjoyed.

On coming to the house, they saw the child with his mother Mary, and they bowed down and worshiped him. Then they opened their treasures and presented him with gifts of gold, frankincense and myrrh.

And having been warned in a dream not to go back to Herod, they returned to their country by another route.

E1 **How does the author's reference to the magi of the Bible help relate to the characters in "The Gift of the Magi"?** (RL.8.9)

  A. It compares the gifts Jim and Della gave to each other to the wise gifts the magi gave to Jesus.

  B. It raises doubts about the sincerity of the reactions of Jim and Della when they each learned what the other had sacrificed.

  C. It contrasts the wealth of the magi to the poverty of Jim and Della, who only had dollars to spend.

  D. This reference is not relevant to the story's characters.

Answer: **A.** The Biblical reference compares the generosity of Jim and Della to that of the wise men.

1.3. INTEGRATION OF KNOWLEDGE AND IDEAS

1. READING: LITERATURE

1.3. INTEGRATION OF KNOWLEDGE AND IDEAS

> ➤ *Directions: Read the passages and answer the questions below.*

THE NECKLACE

She had no gowns, no jewels, nothing. And she loved nothing but that. She felt made for that. She would have liked so much to please, to be envied, to be charming, to be sought after. She had a friend, a former schoolmate at the convent, who was rich, and whom she did not like to go to see any more because she felt so sad when she came home.

But one evening her husband reached home with a triumphant air and holding a large envelope in his hand.

"There," said he, "there is something for you."

She tore the paper quickly and drew out a printed card which bore these words:

The Minister of Public Instruction and Madame Georges Ramponneau request the honor of M. and Madame Loisel's company at the palace of the Ministry on Monday evening, January 18th.Instead of being delighted, as her husband had hoped, she threw the invitation on the table crossly, muttering:

"What do you wish me to do with that?"

"Why, my dear, I thought you would be glad. You never go out, and this is such a fine opportunity. I had great trouble to get it. Everyone wants to go; it is very select, and they are not giving many invitations to clerks. The whole official world will be there."

She looked at him with an irritated glance and said impatiently:

"And what do you wish me to put on my back?"

He had not thought of that. He stammered:

"Why, the gown you go to the theatre in. It looks very well to me."

He stopped, distracted, seeing that his wife was weeping. Two great tears ran slowly from the corners of her eyes toward the corners of her mouth.

"What's the matter? What's the matter?" he answered.

By a violent effort she conquered her grief and replied in a calm voice, while she wiped her wet cheeks:

...continued next page

1. READING: LITERATURE

1.3. INTEGRATION OF KNOWLEDGE AND IDEAS

"Nothing. Only I have no gown, and, therefore, I can't go to this ball. Give your card to some colleague whose wife is better equipped than I am."

He was in despair. He resumed:

"Come, let us see, Mathilde. How much would it cost, a suitable gown, which you could use on other occasions--something very simple?"

She reflected several seconds, making her calculations and wondering also what sum she could ask without drawing on herself an immediate refusal and a frightened exclamation from the economical clerk.

Finally she replied hesitating:

"I don't know exactly, but I think I could manage it with four hundred francs."

CINDERELLA

It happened that the King's son gave a ball, and invited to it all persons of fashion. Our young misses were also invited, for they were quite popular among the people of the countryside. They were highly delighted with the invitation, and wonderfully busy in choosing the gowns, petticoats, and headdresses which might best become them. This made Cinderella's job much harder, for it was she who ironed her sisters' linen and plaited their ruffles. They talked all day long of nothing but how they should be dressed.

"For my part," said the elder, "I will wear my red velvet suit with French trimmings."

"And I," said the younger, "shall wear my usual skirt; but then, to make amends for that I will put on my gold-flowered mantle, and my diamond stomacher, which is far from being the most ordinary one in the world." They sent for the best hairdressers they could get to make up their hair in fashionable style, and bought patches for their cheeks. Cinderella was consulted in all these matters, for she had good taste. She advised them always for the best, and even offered her services to dress their hair, which they were very willing she should do.

As she was doing this, they said to her: "Cinderella, would you not be glad to go to the ball?"

...continued next page

prepaze

1. READING: LITERATURE

> "Young ladies," she said, "you only jeer at me; it is not for such as I am to go there."
>
> "You are right," they replied; "people would laugh to see a poor servant at a ball."

MULTIPLE CHOICE

1. Both passages include a character who (RL.8.9)

    A. is a hairdresser and dressmaker.

    B. is mistreated by her loved ones.

    C. is poor and unpopular.

    D. All of the above

2. Both passages convey a theme of (RL.8.9)

    A. excitement and adventure.   **B.** social class and exclusion.

    C. social injustice and activism.   **D.** fashion trends and economy.

TRUE OR FALSE

3. Both passages use a celebration as the setting for a significant experience in the plot. (RL.8.9)

    A. True   **B.** False

4. The passages differ in style. (RL.8.9)

    A. True   **B.** False

5. In the stories, both women are poor, but Cinderella is socially accepted while Mathilde is not. (RL.8.9)

    A. True   **B.** False

1. 3. INTEGRATION OF KNOWLEDGE AND IDEAS

1. READING: LITERATURE

> ➤ *Directions: Read the passages and answer the questions below.*

THE NECKLACE

The next day she went to her friend and told her of her distress.

Madame Forestier went to a wardrobe with a mirror, took out a large jewel box, brought it back, opened it and said to Madame Loisel:

"Choose, my dear."

She saw first some bracelets, then a pearl necklace, then a Venetian gold cross set with precious stones, of admirable workmanship. She tried on the ornaments before the mirror, hesitated and could not make up her mind to part with them, to give them back. She kept asking:

"Haven't you anymore?"

"Why, yes. Look further; I don't know what you like."

Suddenly she discovered, in a black satin box, a superb diamond necklace, and her heart throbbed with an immoderate desire. Her hands trembled as she took it. She fastened it round her throat, outside her high-necked waist, and was lost in the beauty of her reflection in the mirror.

Then she asked, hesitating, filled with anxious doubt:

"Will you lend me this, only this?"

"Why, yes, certainly."

She threw her arms round her friend's neck, hugged her, and fled with her treasure.

The night of the ball arrived. Madame Loisel was a great success. She was prettier than any other woman present, elegant, graceful, smiling and wild with joy. All the guests looked at her, asked her name, sought to be introduced. All the attaches of the Cabinet wished to waltz with her. She was remarked by the minister himself.

She danced with rapture, forgetting all in the triumph of her beauty, in the glory of her success, in a sort of cloud of happiness comprised of all this homage, admiration, these awakened desires and of that sense of triumph which is so sweet to woman's heart.

...continued next page

1.3. INTEGRATION OF KNOWLEDGE AND IDEAS

1. READING: LITERATURE

CINDERELLA

The fairy then said to Cinderella, "Well, you see here a carriage fit to go to the ball in; are you not pleased with it?"

"Oh, yes!" she cried; "but must I go as I am in these rags?"

Her godmother simply touched her with her wand, and, at the same moment, her clothes were turned into cloth of gold and silver, all decked with jewels. This done, she gave her a pair of the prettiest glass slippers in the whole world. Being thus attired, she got into the carriage, her godmother commanding her, above all things, not to stay till after midnight, and telling her, at the same time, that if she stayed one moment longer, the coach would be a pumpkin again, her horses mice, her coachman a rat, her footmen lizards, and her clothes would become just as they were before.

She promised her godmother she would not fail to leave the ball before midnight. She drove away, scarce able to contain herself for joy. The King's son, who was told that a great princess, whom nobody knew, was come, ran out to meet her. He gave her his hand as she alighted from the coach, and led her into the hall where the company were assembled. There was at once a profound silence; everyone left off dancing, and the violins ceased to play, so attracted was everyone by the singular beauties of the unknown newcomer. Nothing was then heard but a confused sound of voices saying:--

"Ha! how beautiful she is! Ha! how beautiful she is!"

═══ **MULTIPLE CHOICE** ═══

6. **Which of these events occur in both passages?** (RL.8.9)
    A. A party ruins a young woman's life.
    B. An inheritance changes a woman's circumstances.
    C. A woman falls in love and lives happily ever after.
    D. A newfound sense of beauty changes a woman's circumstances.

1. READING: LITERATURE

7. The godmother character in "Cinderella" is comparable to Madame Forestier in "The Necklace." Which word describes both characters? (RL.8.9)

A. Charitable   **B.** Snobbish   **C.** Bossy   **D.** Spiteful

8. Which literary element can be found in both passages? (RL.8.9)

A. Sarcasm   **B.** Irony
C. Figurative language   **D.** Flashback

=== FREE RESPONSE ===

9. How do the characters Mathilde (Madame Loisel) and Cinderella differ? (RL.8.9)

_____

_____

_____

_____

_____

_____

_____

_____

_____

_____

_____

1.3. INTEGRATION OF KNOWLEDGE AND IDEAS

prepaze

1. READING: LITERATURE

> ➢ *Directions: Read the poems and answer the questions below.*

SHALL I COMPARE THEE TO A SUMMER'S DAY? (SONNET 18)

Shall I compare thee to a summer's day?
Thou art more lovely and more temperate.
Rough winds do shake the darling buds of May,
And summer's lease hath all too short a date.
Sometime too hot the eye of heaven shines,
And often is his gold complexion dimmed;
And every fair from fair sometime declines,
By chance, or nature's changing course, untrimmed;
But thy eternal summer shall not fade,
Nor lose possession of that fair thou ow'st,
Nor shall death brag thou wand'rest in his shade,
When in eternal lines to Time thou grow'st.
So long as men can breathe, or eyes can see,
So long lives this, and this gives life to thee.

TO DOROTHY

You are not beautiful, exactly.
You are beautiful, inexactly.
You let a weed grow by the mulberry
and a mulberry grow by the house.
So close, in the personal quiet
of a windy night, it brushes the wall
and sweeps away the day till we sleep.

...continued next page

1. READING: LITERATURE

A child said it, and it seemed true:
"Things that are lost are all equal."
But it isn't true. If I lost you,
the air wouldn't move, nor the tree grow.
Someone would pull the weed, my flower.
The quiet wouldn't be yours. If I lost you,
I'd have to ask the grass to let me sleep.

TRUE OR FALSE

10. **Both poems compare aspects of nature to a woman's beauty.** (RL.8.9)

    A. True   **B.** False

11. **The first poem uses a more modern form of English than the second poem.** (RL.8.9)

    A. True   **B.** False

MULTIPLE CHOICE

12. **Which type of figurative language can be found in both poems?** (RL.8.9)

    A. Personification   **B.** Simile
    C. Onomatopoeia   **D.** Alliteration

13. **Which word best describes the theme conveyed in both poems?** (RL.8.9)

    A. Gloominess   **B.** Admiration
    C. Opposition   **D.** Curiosity

prepaze

1.3. INTEGRATION OF KNOWLEDGE AND IDEAS

1. READING: LITERATURE

> ➤ *Directions: Read the passages and answer the questions below.*

ROMEO AND JULIET ACT II, SCENE II

ROMEO

Lady, by yonder blessed moon I swear
That tips with silver all these fruit-tree tops—

JULIET

O, swear not by the moon, the inconstant moon,
That monthly changes in her circled orb,
Lest that thy love prove likewise variable.

ANNABEL LEE

For the moon never beams without bringing me dreams
Of the beautiful Annabel Lee;
And the stars never rise but I feel the bright eyes
Of the beautiful Annabel Lee;
And so all the night-tide I lie down by the side
Of my darling — my darling — my life and my bride
In the sepulchre there by the sea
In her tomb by the sounding sea

═══════ **FILL IN THE BLANK** ═══════

14. **The** _____ **is a central symbol is both of these works.** (RL.8.9)

15. **The subject of Poe's poem, Annabel Lee, can be compared to the character** _____. (RL.8.9)

16. **The first work is described as a** _____, **while the second is a work of** _____. (RL.8.9)

prepaze

1. READING: LITERATURE

=== MULTIPLE CHOICE ===

17. What is the difference between the two passages? (RL.8.9)

  A. The first passage contains dialogue, while the second does not.

  B. The second passage uses analogies while the first passage does not.

  C. The first passage conveys a theme of love and affection; the second does not.

  D. There are no clear differences between the two passages.

18. How are these passages similar? (RL.8.9)

  A. Both works feature the same characters.

  B. Both works take place in the same setting.

  C. Both works convey a similar theme.

  D. Both works compare the moon to the sea.

=== TRUE OR FALSE ===

19. A modern work can be based on the themes, events, and characters from a traditional work. (RL.8.9)

  A. True   **B.** False

20. A novel cannot be compared to a religious or sacred text. (RL.8.9)

  A. True   **B.** False

1.4. CHAPTER REVIEW

1. READING: LITERATURE

1.4. Chapter Review

> Directions: Read the passage and answer the questions below.

THE DAISY

In the garden close by grew many large and magnificent flowers, and, strange to say, the less fragrance they had the haughtier and prouder they were. The peonies puffed themselves up in order to be larger than the roses, but size is not everything! The tulips had the finest colours, and they knew it well, too, for they were standing bolt upright like candles, that one might see them the better. In their pride they did not see the little daisy, which looked over to them and thought, "How rich and beautiful they are! I am sure the pretty bird will fly down and call upon them. Thank God, that I stand so near and can at least see all the splendour."

And while the daisy was still thinking, the lark came flying down, crying "Tweet," but not to the peonies and tulips—no, into the grass to the poor daisy. Its joy was so great that it did not know what to think. The little bird hopped round it and sang, "How beautifully soft the grass is, and what a lovely little flower with its golden heart and silver dress is growing here." The yellow centre in the daisy did indeed look like gold, while the little petals shone as brightly as silver.

How happy the daisy was! No one has the least idea. The bird kissed it with its beak, sang to it, and then rose again up to the blue sky. It was certainly more than a quarter of an hour before the daisy recovered its senses. Half ashamed, yet glad at heart, it looked over to the other flowers in the garden; surely they had witnessed its pleasure and the honour that had been done to it; they understood its joy. But the tulips stood more stiffly than ever, their faces were pointed and red, because they were vexed. The peonies were sulky; it was well that they could not speak, otherwise they would have given the daisy a good lecture. The little flower could very well see that they were ill at ease, and pitied them sincerely.

1. READING: LITERATURE

=== **MULTIPLE CHOICE** ===

1. **In what way is the daisy's attitude different from the other flowers?** (RL.8.1, RL.8.3)

   A. All of the flowers display a dismal attitude.

   B. The daisy is happy, unlike the roses, tulips and peonies.

   C. The daisy is anxious, unlike the roses, tulips and peonies.

   D. The text does not express the attitudes of the other flowers.

2. **Which line best reveals the tulips' character?** (RL.8.3)

   A. The bird kissed it with its beak, sang to it, and then rose again up to the blue sky.

   B. The peonies were sulky; it was well that they could not speak, otherwise they would have given the daisy a good lecture.

   C. But the tulips stood more stiffly than ever, their faces were pointed and red, because they were vexed.

   D. Its joy was so great that it did not know what to think.

=== **FREE RESPONSE** ===

3. **Write a brief summary of the text.** (RL.8.2)

   _____

   _____

   _____

   _____

   _____

   _____

   _____

1. READING: LITERATURE

_____

_____

_____

_____

_____

_____

_____

_____

> ➤ *Directions: Read the passage and answer the questions below.*

FRANKENSTEIN

As I said this, I suddenly beheld the figure of a man, at some distance, advancing towards me with superhuman speed. He bounded over the crevices in the ice, among which I had walked with caution; his stature, also, as he approached, seemed to exceed that of man. I was troubled: a mist came over my eyes, and I felt a faintness seize me; but I was quickly restored by the cold gale of the mountains. I perceived, as the shape came nearer (sight tremendous and abhorred!) that it was the wretch whom I had created. I trembled with rage and horror, resolving to wait his approach, and then close with him in mortal combat. He approached; his countenance[5] bespoke bitter anguish, combined with disdain and malignity[6], while its unearthly ugliness rendered it almost too horrible for human eyes. But I scarcely observed this; rage and hatred had at first deprived me of utterance, and I recovered only to overwhelm him with words expressive of furious detestation and contempt.

_____

5   A person's facial expression
6   Malicious behavior or nature

prepaze

1. READING: LITERATURE

═══════════════ **MULTIPLE CHOICE** ═══════════════

4. **What is the central idea of this passage?** (RL.8.2)

A. The monster is tracking Frankenstein down to thank him.

B. Frankenstein deeply wishes to help his tortured monster.

C. Frankenstein is trying to attack his monster.

D. Frankenstein is afraid that his monster is trying to attack him.

═══════════════ **TRUE OR FALSE** ═══════════════

5. **Frankenstein appears to be proud of his creation in this text.** (RL.8.1)

A. True   **B.** False

6. **Jealousy is a central theme in this passage.** (RL.8.2)

A. True   **B.** False

➢ *Directions: Read the play and answer the questions below.*

Much Ado About Nothing

ACT I SCENE III. A room in Leonato's house.
Enter **DON JOHN** and **CONRADE**

CONRADE
My lord, why are you thus out of measure sad?

DON JOHN
There is no measure in the occasion that breeds;
therefore the sadness is without limit.

CONRADE
You have of late stood out against your brother: it is needful
that you frame the season for your own harvest.

...continued next page

1. READING: LITERATURE

1.4. CHAPTER REVIEW

DON JOHN

I had rather be a canker in a hedge than a rose in
his grace, and it better fits my blood to be
disdained of all than to fashion a carriage to rob
love from any. Yea, my brother trusts me, but with
a muzzle; therefore I have decreed not to sing in my cage.

CONRADE

Can you make no use of your discontent?

Enter **BORACHIO**

CONRADE

What news, Borachio?

BORACHIO

I can give you intelligence of an intended marriage.

DON JOHN

Will it serve for any model to build mischief on?

BORACHIO

Marry, it is your brother's right hand.

DON JOHN

Who? the most exquisite Claudio?

BORACHIO

He wishes to marry Hero, the daughter and heir of Leonato.
I heard it agreed upon that the
prince should woo Hero for himself, and having
obtained her, give her to Count Claudio.

...continued next page

1. READING: LITERATURE

DON JOHN

This may prove food to my displeasure. That young start-up hath all the glory of my overthrow: if I can cross him any way, I bless myself every way. You are both sure, and will assist me?

CONRADE

To the death, my lord.

=== MULTIPLE CHOICE ===

7. **Which line of dialogue best reveals Don John's mood?** (RL.8.3)
   A. There is no measure in the occasion that breeds; therefore the sadness is without limit.
   B. I had rather be a canker in a hedge than a rose in his grace.
   C. That young start-up hath all the glory of my overthrow: if I can cross him anyway, I bless myself every way.
   D. Yea, my brother trusts me, but with a muzzle; therefore I have decreed not to sing in my cage.

8. **Which line or lines best reveal details about Don John's relationship with his brother?** (RL.8.3)
   A. You have of late stood out against your brother: it is needful that you frame the season for your own harvest.
   B. Yea, my brother trusts me, but with a muzzle; therefore I have decreed not to sing in my cage.
   C. That young start-up hath all the glory of my overthrow: if I can cross him anyway, I bless myself every way.
   D. All of the above

1.4. CHAPTER REVIEW

1. READING: LITERATURE

➤ *Directions: Read the passage and answer the questions below.*

THE CALL OF THE WILD

Spitz was a practiced fighter. From Spitzbergen through the Arctic, and across Canada and the Barrens, he had held his own with all manner of dogs and achieved to mastery over them. Bitter rage was his, but never blind rage. In passion to rend and destroy, he never forgot that his enemy was in like passion to rend and destroy. He never rushed till he was prepared to receive a rush; never attacked till he had first defended that attack.

In vain Buck strove to sink his teeth in the neck of the big white dog. Wherever his fangs struck for the softer flesh, they were countered by the fangs of Spitz. Fang clashed fang, and lips were cut and bleeding, but Buck could not penetrate his enemy's guard. Then he warmed up and enveloped Spitz in a whirlwind of rushes. Time and time again he tried for the snow-white throat, where life bubbled near to the surface, and each time and every time Spitz slashed him and got away.

Then Buck took to rushing, as though for the throat, when, suddenly drawing back his head and curving in from the side, he would drive his shoulder at the shoulder of Spitz, as a ram by which to overthrow him. But instead, Buck's shoulder was slashed down each time as Spitz leaped lightly away. Spitz was untouched, while Buck was streaming with blood and panting hard. The fight was growing desperate. And all the while the silent and wolfish circle waited to finish off whichever dog went down.

=== MULTIPLE CHOICE ===

9.   Which statement best contrasts Spitz and Buck? (RL.8.6)

   A. Spitz is a skilled and vicious fighter, while Buck is not as experienced.

   B. Spitz is a domestic dog, while Buck is a wild dog.

   C. Spitz has fangs, but Buck does not.

   D. Spitz is a mild-mannered dog, while Buck is a ferocious beast.

1. READING: LITERATURE

10. **Which sentence or sentences best describe the difference between Spitz and Buck?** (RL.8.6)

   A. Spitz was untouched, while Buck was streaming with blood and panting hard.

   B. Wherever his fangs struck for the softer flesh, they were countered by the fangs of Spitz.

   C. Time and time again he tried for the snow-white throat, where life bubbled near to the surface, and each time and every time Spitz slashed him and got away.

   D. All of these sentences describe the difference between Spitz and Buck.

11. **How does the contrast between Buck and Spitz help to develop the story's plot?** (RL.8.6)

   A. The contrast between Buck and Spitz depicts them both as heroes.

   B. The contrast between Buck and Spitz helps to build suspense in the plot.

   C. The contrast between Buck and Spitz acts as resolution to a conflict in the story.

   D. The contrast between Buck and Spitz is not closely related to the plot.

> ➤ *Directions: Read the passage and answer the questions below.*

TUCK EVERLASTING

   The constable was fat, and he was sleepy. He wheezed when he spoke. And he spoke quite a bit as they started off, he and the man in the yellow suit. "First they roust me out of bed in the middle of the night, after I been out since sun-up looking for that child, and now I s'pose you're going to try to run me all the way," he said sourly. "I got to tell you this horse of mine is none too strong. I don't have to hurry her as a rule, so most of the time it don't matter. Seems to me we could've waited till dawn, anyway."

...continued next page

1.4. CHAPTER REVIEW

1. READING: LITERATURE

The man in the yellow suit was as courteous as always. "The Fosters have been waiting since yesterday morning," he pointed out. "Naturally, they're very upset. The sooner we get there, the sooner that child will be with them again."

"How come you're so deep in it?" asked the constable suspiciously. "Maybe you're in cahoots with the kidnappers, how do I know? You should of reported it right off, when you saw her get snatched."

The man in the yellow suit sighed. "But of course I had to find out where they were taking her," he explained patiently. "I came right back after that. And the Fosters are friends of mine. They've—uh—sold me their wood."

TRUE OR FALSE

12. The Fosters and the man in the yellow suit have conflicting interests. (RL.8.6)

    A. True   **B.** False

13. The constable's crass nature clashes with the courteous man in the yellow suit. (RL.8.6)

    A. True   **B.** False

14. The man in the yellow suit wants to find the child immediately; the constable is in no rush. (RL.8.6)

    A. True   **B.** False

MULTIPLE CHOICE

15. Which word best describes the interaction between the two characters in this passage? (RL.8.6)

    A. Collaborative   **B.** Incompatible
    C. Understanding   **D.** Inspiring

1. READING: LITERATURE

> *Directions: Read the poems and answer the questions below.*

THE RAVEN

"Be that word our sign in parting, bird or fiend," I shrieked, upstarting-
"Get thee back into the tempest and the Night's Plutonian shore!
Leave no black plume as a token of that lie thy soul hath spoken!
Leave my loneliness unbroken!- quit the bust above my door!
Take thy beak from out my heart, and take thy form from off my door!"
Quoth the Raven, "Nevermore."

And the Raven, never flitting, still is sitting, *still* is sitting
On the pallid bust of Pallas just above my chamber door;
And his eyes have all the seeming of a demon's that is dreaming,
And the lamp-light o'er him streaming throws his shadow on the floor;
And my soul from out that shadow that lies floating on the floor
Shall be lifted- nevermore!

CAGED BIRD

A free bird leaps
on the back of the wind
and floats downstream
till the current ends
and dips his wing
in the orange sun rays
and dares to claim the sky.

But a bird that stalks
down his narrow cage

...continued next page

 prepaze

1. READING: LITERATURE

can seldom see through
his bars of rage
his wings are clipped and
his feet are tied
so he opens his throat to sing.
The caged bird sings

with a fearful trill
of things unknown
but longed for still
and his tune is heard
on the distant hill
for the caged bird
sings of freedom.

MULTIPLE CHOICE

16. **What are the similarities between these two poems?** (RL.8.5)
    A. Both poems have a dark, suspenseful tone.
    B. Both poems have an underlying theme of freedom.
    C. Both poems use birds as symbols.
    D. Both poems follow the same rhyme scheme.

17. **Which line best reveals the narrator's attitude towards the raven in the first poem?** (RL.8.3, RL.8.5)
    A. Take thy beak from out my heart, and take thy form from off my door!"
    B. On the pallid bust of Pallas just above my chamber door...
    C. Quoth the Raven, "Nevermore."
    D. None of the above

1. READING: LITERATURE

18. **How does the form of the second poem contribute to its meaning?** (RL.8.5)

   A. The poem's shift from a free verse to a stricter rhyme scheme symbolizes the bird's experience.

   B. The poem is written in haiku form to simplify the bird's experience.

   C. The poem is written in sonnet form to express the conformity of the bird's experience.

   D. The poem uses humor to form a limerick about the bird's experience.

19. **How does each stanza of the second poem contribute to the structure of the poem?** (RL.8.5)

   A. Each stanza introduces a new character.

   B. Each stanza builds on emotions in a climactic way.

   C. Each stanza explains from a shift to a new narrator.

   D. Each stanza tells its own story and are unrelated.

> ➤ *Directions: Read the poem and answer the questions below.*

1.4. CHAPTER REVIEW

THE NEW COLOSSUS

Not like the brazen giant of Greek fame,
With conquering limbs astride from land to land;
Here at our sea-washed, sunset gates shall stand
A mighty woman with a torch, whose flame
Is the imprisoned lightning, and her name
Mother of Exiles. From her beacon-hand
Glows world-wide welcome; her mild eyes command
The air-bridged harbor that twin cities frame.
"Keep, ancient lands, your storied pomp!" cries she
With silent lips. "Give me your tired, your poor,
Your huddled masses yearning to breathe free,
The wretched refuse of your teeming shore.
Send these, the homeless, tempest-tost to me,
I lift my lamp beside the golden door!"

1. READING: LITERATURE

=== **MULTIPLE CHOICE** ===

20. **This poem is most likely about:** (RL.8.1)

A. Ocean life   **B.** Immigration
C. Taxes   **D.** Overpopulation

21. **The following lines most likely refer to:** (RL.8.1, RL.8.3)

A mighty woman with a torch, whose flame
Is the imprisoned lightning, and her name
Mother of Exiles.

A. The Statue of Liberty   **B.** A famous saint
C. A famous Greek statue.   **D.** A torch that looks like lightning

22. **Which of the following statements best describe the central idea of the poem?** (RL.8.2)

A. The Statue of Liberty greets immigrants as an American symbol of welcome.
B. Many people travel from Greece to America.
C. The Statue of Liberty is an ancient Greek statue that represents fire.
D. None of the above

> ➤ *Directions: Read the passages and answer the questions below.*

THE NECKLACE

She left the ball about four o'clock in the morning. Her husband had been sleeping since midnight in a little deserted anteroom[7]. He threw over her shoulders the wraps he had brought, the modest wraps of common life, the poverty of which contrasted with the elegance of the ball dress. She felt this and wished to escape so as not to be remarked by the other women, who were enveloping themselves in costly furs.

Loisel held her back, saying: "Wait a bit. You will catch cold outside. I will call a cab."

...continued next page

7   Lobby

prepaze   **www.prepaze.com**

1. READING: LITERATURE

But she did not listen to him and rapidly descended the stairs. When they reached the street they could not find a carriage and began to look for one, shouting after the cabmen passing at a distance.

They went toward the Seine in despair, shivering with cold. At last they found on the quay[8] one of those ancient night cabs which, as though they were ashamed to show their shabbiness during the day, are never seen round Paris until after dark.

It took them to their dwelling in the Rue des Martyrs, and sadly they mounted the stairs to their flat. All was ended for her. As to him, he reflected that he must be at the ministry at ten o'clock that morning.

She removed her wraps before the glass so as to see herself once more in all her glory. But suddenly she uttered a cry. She no longer had the necklace around her neck!

Cinderella

Cinderella, indeed, expected such an answer and was very glad of the refusal; for she would have been sadly troubled if her sister had lent her what she jestingly asked for. The next day the two sisters went to the ball, and so did Cinderella, but dressed more magnificently than before. The King's son was always by her side, and his pretty speeches to her never ceased. These by no means annoyed the young lady. Indeed, she quite forgot her godmother's orders to her, so that she heard the clock begin to strike twelve when she thought it could not be more than eleven.

She then rose up and fled, as nimble as a deer. The Prince followed, but could not overtake her. She left behind one of her glass slippers, which the Prince took up most carefully. She got home, but quite out of breath, without her carriage, and in her old clothes, having nothing left her of all her finery but one of the little slippers, fellow to the one she had dropped.

---

8   A platform used for loading and unloading ships

1. READING: LITERATURE

23. **Compare and contrast the events that occur in both passages.** (RL.8.9)

_____

_____

_____

_____

_____

_____

_____

_____

_____

_____

_____

_____

_____

_____

_____

_____

prepaze   **www.prepaze.com**

1. READING: LITERATURE

> ➤ *Directions: Read the passages and answer the questions below.*

The Story of the Big Dipper

Zeus, the king of the gods, fell in love with a mortal woman named Callisto. In a fit of jealousy, Zeus' wife Hera turned Callisto into a bear. She was forced to roam the woods, but Hera let her keep her human memories, making her one sad bear. One day while in the woods, Callisto spotted her son, Arcas. Fully grown, Arcas was an accomplished hunter and, not recognizing his mother, raised his spear to slay the bear. Just in the nick of time, Zeus turned Arcas into a bear who then recognized his mother. Zeus honored both of them by placing them among the stars. He did so by grabbing them by their stubby tails, twirling them around and flinging them into the sky, stretching out the tails. They now represent the constellations of Ursa Major (Big Bear) and Ursa Minor (Little Bear), what we commonly call the Big Dipper and Little Dipper.

The Story of the Big Dipper

The eldest daughter of a large family fell in love with a grizzly bear. Her father was outraged with this and ordered his sons to slay the bear. As the bear died, magic flowed from him to the girl, turning her into a bear. She went on a rampage, killing her mother and father and threatening to kill all eight of her siblings. The eldest son, seeing the helplessness of their plight, shot an arrow into the night sky. All eight children followed it and became the stars we call the Big Dipper. The youngest girl was frightened and hid beside her older brother. Look carefully at the middle star in the Big Dipper's handle. That is Mizar, but right next to it is the much fainter Alcor, representing the frightened young sister of the angry bear.

1.4. CHAPTER REVIEW

=== **FILL IN THE BLANK** ===

24. Both of these stories are myths, which are based on _____ events. (RL.8.9)

25. Both stories feature a conflict involving a _____. (RL.8.9)

 prepaze

1. READING: LITERATURE

=== **MULTIPLE CHOICE** ===

26. **Which of the following would be an example of a modern version of these traditional myths?** (RL.8.9)

   A. A scientific explanation of how the Big Dipper was formed.
   B. A story about boy who studies the history of the Big Dipper.
   C. A story about a man who hunts grizzly bears.
   D. All of the above

=== **TRUE OR FALSE** ===

27. **Conflicting points of view can affect the tone of a text.** (RL.8.6)

   A. True   **B.** False

28. **Two texts with the same structure should also have the same style.** (RL.8.5)

   A. True   **B.** False

29. **The use of dialogue can help to explain why certain events occur in a text.** (RL.8.3)

   A. True   **B.** False

30. **The central message of a story is unrelated to the plot and characters.** (RL.8.2)

   A. True   **B.** False

2. READING: INFORMATIONAL TEXT

2. READING: INFORMATIONAL TEXT

2.1. Key Ideas and Details

Common Core State Standards: CCSS.ELA-LITERACY.RI.8.1, CCSS.ELA-LITERACY.RI.8.2, CCSS.ELA-LITERACY.RI.8.3

Skills:

- Cite the textual evidence that most strongly supports an analysis of what the text says explicitly.
- Draw inferences from the text.
- Determine a central idea of a text and analyze its development over the course of the text.
- Provide an objective summary of the text.
- Analyze how a text makes connections among and distinctions between individuals, ideas, or events.

> **Directions:** Read the passage and answer the questions below.

=== **EXAMPLE** ===

Yellowstone National Park Being Helped By Tire Manufacturer

Tourists visiting Yellowstone National Park's famous geyser, "Old Faithful," will even use tires once they get out of their cars for a closer look. Old Faithful, you see, now boasts a porous, clean, flexible walkway made almost entirely of recycled Michelin tires. The "paved" surface, known as Flexi-Pave and manufactured by the company K.B. Industries (KBI), is kinder to the environment than asphalt because the permeable composite material allows for better erosion control and preservation of the natural patterns of groundwater flow. In addition, the walkway surface is highly durable and tolerant of extreme hot or cold weather, and does not leach any oil into the surrounding environment.

"The Old Faithful Walkway Project is a great example of what a difference a company devoted to sustainability can make in the world's first national park," said Karen Bates Kress, president of the

...continued next page

prep⊙ze   **www.prepaze.com**

2. READING: INFORMATIONAL TEXT

Yellowstone Park Foundation, in a statement. "We are fortunate to have a corporate partner as farsighted, public-spirited and generous as Michelin," she added. Underscoring how important this project was to the 126-year-old tire company, Michelin flew in a team of employees from across the country to help complete the construction of the walkway. The 10 volunteers were winners of a company-wide contest to participate in the project.

Michelin is a major corporate sponsor of the Yellowstone Park Foundation, with a goal of helping the park curb operating expenses and reduce the consumption of raw materials. To ensure this, Michelin regularly donates and helps maintain thousands of tires for Yellowstone National Park's more than 800 vehicles, including patrol cars, garbage trucks, snow plows and load-hauling tractor trailers. The tires feature the latest in green tire technology to help save fuel and reduce emissions.

E1 What can the reader logically infer about the Michelin company?
(RI.8.1)

A. Michelin supports Yellowstone in order to sell more tires.

B. Yellowstone needs more walkways made of tires.

C. Michelin is reducing waste by its contribution to Yellowstone.

D. Yellowstone depends on Michelin to maintain its park vehicles.

Answer: C. Based on the phrase, "reduce the consumption of raw materials," the reader can make the assumption that Michelin's contributions of old tires helps in lessening waste.

> ➤ *Directions: Read the passage and answer the questions below.*

=== **EXAMPLE** ===

Pablo Picasso was one of the most innovative artists in history. He created over 20,000 unique works of art. His paintings and sculptures

...continued next page

2.1. KEY IDEAS AND DETAILS

2. READING: INFORMATIONAL TEXT

were groundbreaking due to new styles such as collage art. This style creates abstract illusions with various shapes and textures. He was also known for his ability to construct three-dimensional art. These techniques are still admired and recreated in modern art. Picasso's influence will continue to inspire artists for many years to come.

E2 **What is the central idea of this passage?** (RI.8.2)

    A. Pablo Picasso was one of the most innovative artists in history.

    B. Pablo Picasso was born in Spain and this distracted from his work.

    C. He was also known for his ability to construct three-dimensional art.

    D. Pablo Picasso loved to paint.

Answer: **A.** The central idea of a text is the author's main point. The central idea of this passage is that Pablo Picasso was one of the most innovative artists in history.

EXAMPLE

Cavities can be a very serious dental problem. The good news is that they can be prevented. Cavities are caused by unhealthy food choices and poor oral hygiene. Sugary snacks are delicious, but can be harmful for your teeth. It is best to avoid these foods in order to prevent cavities. Also, brushing and flossing your teeth twice a day can reduce the risk of cavities. There is no need to worry about cavities if you make the right choices.

E3 **How does this passage explore cause and effect?** (RI.8.3)

    A. The text explains how sugary snacks lead to stomach aches.

    B. The text explains how to brush your teeth in a daily routine.

    C. The text explains how making good choices can prevent cavities.

    D. The text explains why dentists are important.

Answer: **C.** The text explains how making good choices can prevent cavities. Cause and effect demonstrates how one event leads to another.

2. READING: INFORMATIONAL TEXT

> ➤ *Directions: Read the passage and answer the questions below.*

Astro Boy: More Than Just A Cartoon

Often called "The Mickey Mouse of Japan," Astro Boy was created in 1952 by Tezuka Osamu, Japan's most influential cartoonist. Tezuka's characters, with their large eyes and expressive faces, established the drawing style used in all anime today.

But it was Tezuka's storytelling that made Astro Boy popular with audiences around the world. Astro Boy re-imagines the story of Pinocchio in a futuristic setting. Although Astro Boy is a powerful robot with protects the Earth, he is, at heart, a little boy with an innocent view of the world. Themes in the Astro Boy story include respect for life and a clear anti-bigotry message. But these themes are presented humorously, with some seriously funny results.

Children today can experience Astro Boy outside of manga and anime. For example, D3Publisher of America, Inc., has created a video game that allows children to become Astro Boy. Available on Wii, DS, PS2 and PSP, Astro Boy: The Video Game combines entertaining gameplay with interesting storytelling. Players of all ages can use Astro Boy's weapons to battle enemies and unlock different versions of the character. Based on the 2009 full-length CG film, the video game features the voices of Freddie Highmore and Kristen Bell and allows players to explore environments from the movie.

Astro Boy emerged from post-World War II Japan, when instability and the fear of technology played a major role in popular culture. But while other Japanese movies involved giant monsters like Godzilla destroying Toyko, Tezuka created a more reassuring vision. As Tezuka once said, "Love all the creatures! Love everything that has life! I have been trying to express this message in every one of my works."

 prepaze

2. READING: INFORMATIONAL TEXT

=== **MULTIPLE CHOICE** ===

1. **Which of the following can be inferred from the article?** (RI.8.1)

   A. Astro Boy is the most popular Japanese cartoon.

   B. Astro Boy is primarily popular just in Japan.

   C. Without Astro Boy's popularity, anime would not look like it does.

   D. As soon as he was introduced, Astro Boy became popular.

2. **What is the main idea of this article?** (RI.8.2)

   A. Astro Boy is referred to as "the Mickey Mouse of Japan."

   B. This one cartoon character has spread throughout the world in many forms.

   C. Tezuka's purpose was to get people to enjoy different types of cartoon characters.

   D. Astro Boy is a powerful robot who guards the Earth.

3. **What is the author's attitude about Astro Boy?** (RI.8.1)

   A. The author is an admirer of the character and his traits.

   B. The author does not express an opinion on Astro Boy .

   C. The author is not a fan of the anime style.

   D. The author thinks Astro Boy needs some improvement.

> ➤ *Directions: Read the passage and answer the questions below.*

Not The Brakes Or The Engine; It's The Tires That keep You Safe

The four tires on your family car are the only thing connecting it to the road, and they play a critical role in your safety. Given their part in keeping you safe, it's worth taking the time to take care of your tires.

Nearly 100 million Americans are expected to have taken a family vacation by year's end, with spring and summer road trips topping many of their plans. With so many Americans on the road all year long, tire damage is an unfortunate reality.

...continued next page

2. READING: INFORMATIONAL TEXT

According to one study, some of the most common causes of tire damage are running over something, such as a curb (72%), nails (70%), or potholes (39%). Other common causes of tire damage are more easily preventable, such as driving with bald tires (48%) and driving on a tire with low air pressure (44%).

What's the one location you probably most want to avoid when driving? Construction zones, where many tires are punctured by spikes, wrenches, screwdrivers and pliers.

"The four tires on your vehicle are the only parts to come in contact with and keep you connected to the road," notes Jess Egerton, director of tire development at a company that has been making tires since 1914. "That's why, for safety and performance reasons, you have to properly care for, maintain and inspect them."

2.1. KEY IDEAS AND DETAILS

=== **MULTIPLE CHOICE** ===

4.   What is the central idea of this text? (RI.8.2)

A. Punctured tires can be very dangerous.

B. Most people do not check their tires regularly.

C. Good tires are a crucial element in car safety .

D. Nearly 100 million Americans will travel by car this holiday.

5.   Which best describes the type of connections seen in this article? (RI.8.3)

A. Statistics

B. Cause and effect

C. Compare and contrast

D. Classification

6.   What best explains how the first sentence in the first and last paragraphs work? (RI.8.3)

A. The first points out how to care for tires; the last does not.

B. The two sentences both stress the importance of tires.

C. The first explains how to avoid tire problems, but the last skips that.

D. They both explain what Jess Egerton means.

2. READING: INFORMATIONAL TEXT

2.1. KEY IDEAS AND DETAILS

7.   What is the problem in the second paragraph? (RI.8.5)

    A. There are no statistics backing up the claim of 100 million American travelers.

    B. The paragraph deals with vacations and travel, not tires.

    C. There is no mention of what year the author is talking about.

    D. The author talks about 100 million travelers in spring and summer and then says "all year long."

8.   Which sentence below best explains the author's main point? (RI.8.3)

    A. Tires are important in helping to prevent accidents.

    B. Tires need to be properly maintained.

    C. Tire damage can occur in many ways.

    D. Tire damage mostly happens in construction zones.

> ➤ *Directions: Read the passage and answer the questions below.*

> Most people think that sharks are harmful to human beings. In reality, humans are actually more of a threat to sharks. Every year, millions of sharks are harmed by people. This is compared to less than 100 people who are attacked by sharks per year. Many attacks on sharks are unprovoked. This means that sharks may be unexpectedly abused while swimming innocently in the ocean. While sharks can indeed be dangerous, they are usually harmless.

MULTIPLE CHOICE

9.   Which sentence best describes the central idea of this passage? (RI.8.2)

    A. Most people think that sharks are harmful to human beings.

    B. Humans are actually more of a threat to sharks than vice versa.

    C. Many attacks on sharks are unprovoked.

    D. Sharks can be very dangerous.

2. READING: INFORMATIONAL TEXT

10. **Which sentence best supports the central idea of this passage?** (RI.8.2)

    A. Every year, millions of sharks are harmed by people.

    B. Most people think that sharks are harmful to human beings.

    C. Some people like to swim with sharks.

    D. Sharks like to eat small fish.

11. **Which sentence could also describe the central idea of this passage?** (RI.8.2)

    A. Sharks are a type of fish.

    B. Sharks can be very harmful to humans.

    C. Shark attacks are less common than human attacks on sharks.

    D. Sharks are very good swimmers.

12. **Which sentence does NOT support the central idea of this passage?** (RI.8.2)

    A. Every year, millions of sharks are harmed by people.

    B. Many attacks on sharks are unprovoked.

    C. While sharks can indeed be dangerous, they are usually harmless.

    D. People should beware of sharks.

> ➤ *Directions: Read the passage and answer the questions below.*

What Exactly Is A Public Domain Work Of Literature?

As of 2019, copyright has expired for all works published in the United States before 1924. In other words, if the work was published in the U.S. before January 1, 1924, you are free to use it in the U.S. without permission. These rules and dates apply regardless of whether the work was created by an individual author, a group of authors, or an employee (a work made for hire).

Because of legislation passed in 1998, no new works fell into the public domain between 1998 and 2018 due to expiration. In 2019, works published in 1923 expired. In 2020, works published in 1924 will expire, and so on.

...continued next page

2.1. KEY IDEAS AND DETAILS

prepaze

2. READING: INFORMATIONAL TEXT

For works published after 1977, if the work was written by a single author, the copyright will not expire until 70 years after the author's death. If a work was written by several authors and published after 1977, it will not expire until 70 years after the last surviving author dies.

=== FILL IN THE BLANK ===

2.1. KEY IDEAS AND DETAILS

13. **The text shows the difference between books written before _____ and those written after_____.** (RI.8.1)

14. **The text structure seen in this passage is best described as _____ _____.** (RI.8.3)

15. **According to the text, the copyright on a book written by several people will expire 70 years _____.** (RI.8.1)

16. **The restriction made in the text about countries only applies to _____.** (RI.8.1)

=== TRUE OR FALSE ===

17. **The central idea of a text should be fully developed within the first paragraph.** (RI.8.2)

    A. True   **B.** False

18. **Since the central idea is what the text is mainly about, there should only be one central idea.** (RI.8.2)

    A. True   **B.** False

                   www.prepaze.com

2. READING: INFORMATIONAL TEXT

19. **An inference is a personal opinion about the details of a text.** (RI.8.1)

    A. True   **B.** False

20. **Categorizing is a strategy used when making connections within a text.** (RI.8.3)

    A. True   **B.** False

2.1. KEY IDEAS AND DETAILS

2.2. CRAFT AND STRUCTURE

2. READING: INFORMATIONAL TEXT

~~~~ 2.2. Craft and Structure ~~~~

Common Core State Standards: CCSS.ELA-LITERACY.RI.8.4, CCSS.ELA-LITERACY.RI.8.5, CCSS.ELA-LITERACY.RI.8.6

Skills:
- Determine the meaning of words and phrases as they are used in a text, including figurative, connotative, and technical meanings.
- Analyze the impact of specific word choices on meaning and tone.
- Analyze in detail the structure of a specific paragraph in a text.
- Determine an author's point of view or purpose in a text.
- Analyze how the author acknowledges and responds to conflicting evidence or viewpoints.

> ➢ *Directions: Read the passage and answer the questions below.*

=== **EXAMPLE** ===

Raisins are versatile snacks and contain many beneficial nutrients. Candy is extremely sweet and can cause tooth decay. In contrast, raisins are both sweet and healthy. Another advantage is that raisins can be used to make other healthy snacks. Pastries such as bread and muffins can be much healthier than sugary treats. Plus, raisins come from grapes. Grapes go through an intricate drying process in order to become raisins. This magical transformation makes them even more interesting! So whenever you want a snack, try some delicious raisins.

E1   What is the meaning of the word *intricate*? (RI.8.4)

A. Hydrated   **B.** Confusing
C. Complicated   **D.** Destructive

Answer: **C.** The word *intricate* means complicated in the context of this text.

2. READING: INFORMATIONAL TEXT

E2 **What is the structure and key concept of this sentence?** (RI.8.5)

In contrast, raisins are both sweet and healthy.

A. This sentence uses a personal narrative to explain how raisins are a form of dehydrated grapes.

B. This sentence uses classification to explain how raisins are a form of dehydrated grapes.

C. This sentence compares raisins to candy to highlight the flavor similarities.

D. This sentence contrasts raisins and candy to highlight the health benefits of raisins.

Answer: **D.** This sentence contrasts raisins and candy to highlight the health benefits of raisins.

E3 **What is the author's purpose in this text?** (RI.8.6)

A. To inform readers about raisins.

B. To persuade readers to eat more raisins.

C. Both A and C

D. None of the above

Answer: **C.** The author's purpose is to persuade readers to eat more raisins. The author uses informative details about raisins in order to support his/her purpose.

2.2. CRAFT AND STRUCTURE

prepaze

2. READING: INFORMATIONAL TEXT

> ➢ *Directions: Read the passage and answer the questions below.*

DOROTHY PAYNE, QUAKERESS:
A SIDE-LIGHT UPON THE CAREER OF 'DOLLY' MADISON

Tuesday, Aug. 23rd, 1814

Dear Sister:

My husband left yesterday morning to join General Winder. He inquired anxiously whether I had courage or firmness to remain in the President's house until his return on the morrow, or succeeding day; and on my assurance that I had no fear but for him and the success of our army, he left me, beseeching me to take care of myself, and of the cabinet papers, public and private.

I have since received two dispatches from him, written with a pencil; but the last is alarming, because he desires I should be ready at a moment's warning to enter my carriage and leave the city; that the enemy seemed stronger than had been reported, and that it might happen that they would reach the city with intention to destroy it.... I am accordingly ready; I have pressed as many cabinet papers into trunks as will fill one carriage; our private property must be sacrificed, as it is impossible to procure wagons for its transportation. I am determined not to go myself until I see Mr. Madison safe, and he can accompany me—as I hear of much hostility towards him ... disaffection stalks arounds us.... My friends and acquaintances are all gone,—even Colonel C—with his hundred men, who were stationed as a guard in the enclosure.

=== **MULTIPLE CHOICE** ===

1. **What does the word *assurance* mean?** (RI.8.4)

    ... and on my <u>assurance</u> that I had no fear but for him and the success of our army, he left me ...

    A. A sense of confidence

    B. A sense of uncertainty

    C. A pact or treaty

    D. A type of security used in the army

2. READING: INFORMATIONAL TEXT

2. **What does the word *disaffection* mean?** (RI.8.4)

... <u>disaffection</u> stalks arounds us ...
A. An increasing feeling of affection
B. An increasing feeling of discord and conflict
C. An absence of privacy
D. A decrease in population

═══════════════ **TRUE OR FALSE** ═══════════════

3. **The underlined phrase indicates that Dolly should be prepared for sudden danger.** (RI.8.4, RI.8.5)

... but the last is alarming, because he desires I should be <u>ready at a moment's warning</u> to enter my carriage and leave the city ...

A. True   **B.** False

4. **The letter structure of the text reveals Dolly's thoughts and characteristics.** (RI.8.5)

A. True   **B.** False

> *Directions: Read the passage and answer the questions below.*

People eat pasta all over the world. Pasta originated in Italy, but there are actually over 100 varieties of pasta available internationally. They come in a wide range of shapes, sizes, and textures. The type of ingredients used may differ as well. The one thing that these pasta have in common is that they are enjoyed by diners worldwide.

Pasta is a staple in Asian cuisine. Asian pasta is long and thin, similar to spaghetti, but is cooked and eaten in a different style. In China, Mein noodles are traditionally stir-fried and served with meat and vegetables. Japanese Ramen noodles are served in a fish broth with toppings such as seaweed and onions. The Korean dish, bibim guksu, is served with cold noodles. These are just a few of the many ways pasta is eaten in Asian countries.

...continued next page

2.2. CRAFT AND STRUCTURE

 prepaze

2. READING: INFORMATIONAL TEXT

Couscous is a well-known pasta in North African regions. The small, round pasta is often eaten in places such as Algeria and Egypt. It is usually served with stew made from meat, vegetables, and chickpeas. In Morocco, couscous is sprinkled with almonds, cinnamon, and sugar for dessert. The size, texture and various styles of this pasta make it very unique.

In the United States, pasta is a dinnertime favorite. Macaroni and cheese is one of the most popular pasta meals in the country. Other dishes, such as Fettucine Alfredo, are inspired by Italian tradition but adapted to American culture. This is a common example of how pasta has influenced international foods since its origin in Italy.

In Italy, of course, pasta is an essential component in the national cuisine. Italian pasta dishes are famous for their special sauces, herbs, and flavors. It is also served with a variety of meats and cheeses. Many people travel to Italy in order to experience the birthplace of pasta. But many, thanks to worldwide availability, can enjoy pasta at home anywhere.

MULTIPLE CHOICE

5. What is the author's purpose in this text? (RI.8.6)

A. To entertain readers with a story about pasta

B. To inform readers about the origins and varieties of pasta

C. To persuade readers to eat authentic Italian pasta

D. To share the author's personal pasta making experience

6. Which sentence or sentences best help to identify the author's purpose? (RI.8.6)

A. People eat pasta all over the world.

B. Pasta originated in Italy, but there are actually over 100 varieties of pasta available internationally.

C. They come in a wide range of shapes, sizes, and textures.

D. All of the above

2. READING: INFORMATIONAL TEXT

> *Directions: Read the advertisement and answer the questions below.*

15 EPIC REASONS TO VISIT CHICAGO

A guy once said, make no little plans. In other words, be part of something big today. Be part of something bigger than yourself. Be part of a city that's larger than life — Chicago. This city is buzzing with energy. Plan to soak it up. Prepare to lose yourself in it. But most importantly, plan your trip now! Here are 15 epic reasons to visit Chicago.

From gourmet to street, Italian to Taiwanese, the fusion of food in Chicago is astounding and there are over 5,195 restaurants to eat through. The city is home to some of the world's most elite chefs at the forefront of cutting-edge cuisine. From Michelin star restaurants and 40+ James Beard Award medalists to an overflow of four- and five-diamond winners every year, the dining scene has never been more thrilling.

One of Chicago's greatest achievements is its skyline, complete with architectural stunners such as the Wrigley Building, Willis Tower and Trump International Hotel & Tower. Float down the Chicago River on an architectural boat tour by kayak or cruise ship, or go sky high by helicopter tour. Check out one of the eye-opening options from one of the 85 Chicago Architecture Foundation tours, offered an astonishing 6,000 times per year. Get swept up in panoramic views of the city from 103 stories up at The Ledge at Skydeck Chicago or from the 94th floor of the TILT experience at 360° CHICAGO (formerly John Hancock Observatory).

Chicago as a beach vacation? You bet! The lakefront is hopping in the summer as Chicagoans take to 26 sandy beaches. Dip your toes into the cool blue waters of Lake Michigan from Memorial Day to Labor Day. Here you can kick back with a cool beverage at Montrose Beach, play volleyball at lively North Avenue Beach, let the kids run wild at 31st Street Beach or soak up the sun at peaceful 63rd Street Beach.

Getting into — and out of — Chicago is a breeze, thanks to award-winning O'Hare and Midway international airports; frequent passenger service with Amtrak trains; and a network of major highways. Situated squarely in the center of the country, Chicago is accessible from virtually anywhere. Chicago's booming hotel industry makes for plenty of accommodation options, from the intimate to the extravagant, and with prime locations close to everything Chicago has to offer.

2.2. CRAFT AND STRUCTURE

2. READING: INFORMATIONAL TEXT

=== FILL IN THE BLANK ===

7. The author's purpose is to _____ and
    _____readers about Chicago and its attractions. (RI.8.6)

8. The author has a _____ point of view towards the topic. (RI.8.6)

=== TRUE OR FALSE ===

9. The text is based on the author's personal point of view about
    visiting Chicago. (RI.8.6)

    A. True   **B.** False

10. The text is a personal narrative recalling the author's visit to
    Chicago. (RI.8.5, RI.8.6)

    A. True   **B.** False

> *Directions: Read the passage and answer the questions below.*

The First Climate Change Scientist

In a series of experiments conducted in 1856, Eunice Newton Foote — a scientist and women's rights campaigner from Seneca Falls, New York — became the first person to discover that altering the proportion of carbon dioxide in the atmosphere would change its temperature. This relationship between carbon dioxide and the earth's climate has since become one of the key principles of modern meteorology, the greenhouse effect, and climate science.

She wrote: "An atmosphere [with excess carbon dioxide] would give our earth a high temperature; and if as some suppose, at one period of its history the air had mixed with it a larger proportion than at present, an increased temperature...must have necessarily resulted."

Foote's experiment was ingeniously homemade. Using four thermometers, two glass cylinders, and an air pump, she isolated the gases that make up the atmosphere and exposed them to the sun's rays, both in sunlight and in shade.

...continued next page

2. READING: INFORMATIONAL TEXT

Measuring the change in their temperatures, she discovered that carbon dioxide and water vapor absorbed enough heat that this absorption could affect climate. However, no one acknowledged that Foote was the first to make this discovery for more than a century, in large part because she was a woman.

Entirely because she was a woman, Foote was barred from reading the paper describing her findings at the 1856 meeting of the American Association for the Advancement of Science held in Albany, New York. Instead, Professor Joseph Henry of the Smithsonian had the honor of doing so. Unfortunately, "indifference" would be the best word to describe how her findings were received.

Not only was Foote not permitted to read her groundbreaking paper, she was passed over for publication in the Association's annual Proceedings. "Circumstances Affecting the Heat of Sun's Rays" was published in its entirety in The American Journal of Science (September 1856) — but did not have her name attached to it in any way.

=== **MULTIPLE CHOICE** ===

11. **Which phrase describes how the scientists saw Foote?** (RI 8.4)

A. "did not have her name attached to it"
B. "barred from reading the paper"
C. "no one acknowledged"
D. "Unfortunately, 'indifference' would be"

12. **What is the key concept in Foote's experiment? (RI.8.5)**

A. Too much carbon dioxide has been in the atmosphere before.
B. Too much carbon dioxide is impossible.
C. Too much carbon dioxide heats the atmosphere.
D. Too much carbon dioxide is a result of a heated atmosphere.

13. **Which sentence below means the closest to "This relationship between carbon dioxide and the earth's climate has since become one of the key principles of modern meteorology, the greenhouse effect, and climate science"?** (RL8.4)

     A. What Foote proved happens in the atmosphere has caused a lot of controversy about the greenhouse effect.

     B. Foote's discoveries about carbon dioxide led to modern studies of how it affects life today.

     C. Carbon dioxide and the earth's climate caused the development of climate science.

     D. Modern scientific study of the atmosphere came right from Foote's experiments on the greenhouse effect.

14. **Details in the article help develop the author's second key point. What is it?** (RI.8.5)

     A. Foote proved the greenhouse effect is real.

     B. Foote's discoveries were held up because she was a woman.

     C. Too much carbon dioxide is a problem we must confront.

     D. Foote was able to do her experiments with very few tools.

15. **What is the purpose of this text?** (RI.8.6)

     A. The text is written is to persuade readers to study science.

     B. The text is written to argue in favor of female scientists.

     C. The text is written as a story to entertain the reader.

     D. The text is written to show a female scientist's conrtibutions.

➢ *Directions: Read the passage and answer the questions below*

THE WHITE HOUSE COOKBOOK

Carving is one important acquisition in the routine of daily living. Everyone should try to attain the ability to do it well, and also gracefully.

When carving, use a chair slightly higher than the ordinary size, as it gives a better position on the meat. Carving while seated appears more graceful than when standing, as is often quite necessary when carving a turkey, or a very large joint. Skill is more important than strength.

2. READING: INFORMATIONAL TEXT

The platter should be placed opposite, and sufficiently nearby to give perfect command of the item to be carved. The knife should be of medium size, sharp with a keen edge. Commence by cutting the slices thin, laying them carefully to one side of the platter. Afterwards, place the desired amount on each guest's plate.

MULTIPLE CHOICE

16. What is the meaning of the word _acquisition_ as it is used in the sentence? (RI.8.4)

Carving is one important <u>acquisition</u> in the routine of daily living.
- **A.** The purchase of a food item
- **B.** A useful skill to have for life
- **C.** The use of a sharp object
- **D.** A type of cooking technique

17. What is the meaning of the underlined phrase? (RI.8.4)

The knife should be of medium size, sharp with a <u>keen edge</u>.
- **A.** A fancy engraved handle
- **B.** An intelligent style
- **C.** A piercing blade
- **D.** None of the above

18. Which of the following best describes the structure of this text? (RI.8.5)
- **A.** Compare and contrast
- **B.** Narrative
- **C.** Cause and effect
- **D.** Description

FREE RESPONSE

19. How does the structure of the text develop the author's purpose? (RI.8.6)

_____

_____

2.2. CRAFT AND STRUCTURE

2. READING: INFORMATIONAL TEXT

_____

_____

_____

_____

_____

_____

_____

20. **What is the role of the first lines of the text?** (RI.8.5)

Carving is one important acquisition in the routine of daily living. Everyone should try to attain the ability to do it well, and also gracefully.

_____

_____

_____

_____

_____

_____

_____

_____

2.3. INTEGRATION OF KNOWLEDGE AND IDEAS

www.prepaze.com

2. READING: INFORMATIONAL TEXT

~~~ 2.3. Integration of Knowledge and Ideas ~~~

Common Core State Standards: CCSS.ELA-LITERACY.RI.8.7, CCSS.ELA-LITERACY.RI.8.8, CCSS.ELA-LITERACY.RI.8.9

Skills:

- Evaluate the advantages and disadvantages of using different mediums (e.g., print or digital text, video, multimedia) to present a particular topic or idea.
- Evaluate the argument and specific claims in a text.
- Analyze a case in which two or more texts provide conflicting information on the same topic.

=== **EXAMPLE** ===

> ➤ *Directions: Read the question and select the best answer choice.*

E1 **Which medium would be the best for presenting information about mudslides?** (RI.8.7)

    A. Print   **B.** Audio

    C. Video   **D.** None of the above

Answer: **C.** In order to demonstrate an actual mudslide, a video would be the best medium.

E2 **An author is writing a persuasive article about the protection of endangered species. The author believes that the community has already provided enough resources and protection for these endangered animals. What evidence could the author include in order to support her claim?** (RI.8.8)

    A. Data from a local conservation organization

    B. Photos of an endangered animal

    C. A quote from a community resident who loves animals

    D. A chart indicating the life expectancy of an endangered animal

Answer: **A.** The author could contact a local conservation organization to obtain data about community resources. This is the most credible source of evidence.

2. READING: INFORMATIONAL TEXT

=== **EXAMPLE** ===

E3 **A student is conducting research about a soldier's life during World War II. One source is an online encyclopedia article about the average life of a World War II soldier. Another source is a script from an interview conducted with a World War II veteran. Explain how these texts could provide conflicting information on the same topic.** (RI.8.9)

Answer: Since the primary source interview is with a particular veteran, his or her experience may vary slightly from a general text about a soldier's life during World War II.

> ➢ *Directions: Read the question and select the best answer choice.*

2.3. INTEGRATION OF KNOWLEDGE AND IDEAS

1. **Why might the audience need to hear the tone of a speaker in an audio speech?** (RI.8.7)

   A. The message would be stated in a clearer format.

   B. The audience may not be able to see very well.

   C. The audience could sense the additional meaning that voice emphasis provides.

   D. The audience would not enjoy reading the speech instead.

2. **A student is presenting a report about how commercial farms affect the local economy. Which medium would be best to use?** (RI.8.7)

   A. Audio text

   B. Graphic information

   C. Quoted material from an opinion piece

   D. None of the above

2. READING: INFORMATIONAL TEXT

3. **Angela is looking for information about the controversy surrounding the story about George Washington and the cherry tree. She knows that some resources report that the story is true, while others report that it is false. What can Angela do to find more credible information?** (RI.8.9)

   A. Research primary sources regarding the cherry tree story.
   B. Read opinions about that story on the Internet.
   C. Consult an encyclopedia about George Washington.
   D. Read the biography of George Washington.

4. **Which of the following is most likely true regarding discrepancies in resource information?** (RI.8.9)

   A. Information should not always be trusted just because it is published.
   B. Some authors are trying to deceive readers with false information.
   C. Both sets of information are probably incorrect.
   D. Conducting research is discouraged due to conflicting information.

> ➤ *Directions: Read the passage and answer the questions below.*

THE LOGIC OF VEGETARIANISM

The term "vegetarian," as applied to those who abstain from all meats, but not necessarily from such animal products (such as eggs, milk, and cheese), appears to have come into existence over fifty years ago. This was around the time that the Vegetarian Society was founded back in 1847. Until that date, no special name had been appropriated for the reformed diet system, which was usually known as the "Pythagorean" or "vegetable diet." Presumably, it was felt that when the movement grew in volume, it was in need of an original and distinctive title. The question is whether or not the name "vegetarian" was wisely or unwisely chosen. This is a question on which there has been some difference of opinion among food reformers themselves. It is possible that adverse criticism would have been strongly expressed, except for the fact that no better title has been given.

...continued next page

2.3. INTEGRATION OF KNOWLEDGE AND IDEAS

Copyrighted Material **prepaze**

2. READING: INFORMATIONAL TEXT

On the whole, the name "vegetarian" seems to be fairly serviceable. The disadvantage of this term is that it leaves room for argument on the part of its opponents. In all controversies, such as that of which vegetarianism is the subject, there are verbalists who cannot see beyond the outer shell of a word to the thing which the word signifies. They delight to chop logic and raise small obstacles as thus:

Verbalist: Why "vegetarian?"

Vegetarian: Why not "vegetarian?"

Verbalist: How can it be consistent with vegetarianism to consume, as you admit you do, milk, butter, cheese, and eggs, all of which are choice foods from the animal kingdom?

Vegetarian: That entirely depends on what is meant by "vegetarianism."

Verbalist: Well, surely its meaning is obvious—a diet of vegetables only, with no particle of animal substance.

Vegetarian: As a matter of fact, such is not, and has never been, its accepted meaning. The question was often debated in the early years of the Vegetarian Society, and it was always held that the use of eggs and milk was not prohibited. "To induce habits of abstinence from the flesh of animals (fish, flesh, fowl) as food" was the original aim of vegetarianism, as officially stated on the title-page of its journal.

Verbalist: But the word "vegetarian"—what other meaning can it have than that which I have attributed to it?

Vegetarian: Presumably those who invented the word were the best judges of its meaning, and what they meant by it is proved beyond a doubt by the usage of the society.

MULTIPLE CHOICE

5. **What is Salt's overall claim in this argumentative text?** (RI.8.8)

   A. People should practice vegetarianism in order to protect animal rights.

   B. The term "vegetarian" should have changed over the years.

   C. The term "vegetarian" is appropriate, although misunderstood title.

   D. Verbalists should switch to vegetarianism.

2. READING: INFORMATIONAL TEXT

6. In what way could Salt strengthen his argument? (RI.8.8)

A. Include a study about the use of the term "vegetarian."

B. Provide direct quotes from verbalists about their viewpoint.

C. Explain why so many people do not fully understand the meaning of a "vegetarian."

D. Describe a typical daily meal for a vegetarian.

7. According to Salt's argument, how has the term "vegetarians" changed since the term was first coined? (RI.8.8)

A. There is no evidence explained in this argument regarding the changes.

B. There has been a significant change with the term.

C. There has been a slight change with the term.

D. The term has not changed.

➢ *Directions: Read the passage and answer the questions below.*

THE LIFE OF CHRISTOPHER COLUMBUS

Christopher Columbus was born in the Republic of Genoa. The honor of his birth-place has been claimed by many villages in that Republic, and the house in which he was born cannot be now pointed out with certainty. But the best authorities agree that the children and the grown people of the world have never been mistaken when they have said: "America was discovered in 1492 by Christopher Columbus, a native of Genoa."

Christopher Columbus was the oldest son of Dominico Colombo and Suzanna Fontanarossa. This name means Red-fountain. He had two brothers, Bartholomew and Diego, whom we shall meet again. Diego is the Spanish way of writing the name which we call James.

It seems probable that Christopher was born in the year 1436, though some writers have said that he was older than this, and some that he was younger. The record of his birth and that of his baptism have not been found.

...continued next page

2. READING: INFORMATIONAL TEXT

His father was not a rich man, but he was able to send Christopher, as a boy, to the University of Pavia, and here he studied grammar, geometry, geography and navigation, astronomy and the Latin language. But this was as a boy studies, for in his fourteenth year he left the university and entered, in hard work, on "the larger college of the world." If the date given above, of his birth, is correct, this was in the year 1450, a few years before the Turks took Constantinople, and, in their invasion of Europe, affected the daily life of everyone, young or old, who lived in the Mediterranean countries. From this time, for fifteen years, it is hard to trace along the life of Columbus.

AMERICAN LEADERS AND HEROES

More than four hundred and fifty years ago there lived in the city of Genoa a poor working man, who made his living by preparing wool for the spinners. Of his four sons, the eldest was Christopher, born in 1436. Young Christopher was not, so far as we know, very different from most other boys in Genoa. He doubtless joined in their every-day sports, going with them to see the many vessels that sailed in and out of that famous sea-port, and listening for hours to the stories of sailors about distant lands.

But he did not spend all his time in playing and visiting the wharves, for we know that he learned his father's trade, and in school studied, among other things, reading, arithmetic, grammar, geography, and map-drawing. We can easily believe that he liked geography best of all, since it would carry his imagination far out over the sea and to lands beyond the sea. In map-drawing he acquired such skill that when he became a man he could earn his living, when occasion demanded, by making maps and charts.

Beyond these facts little is known about the boyhood and youth of Columbus. Very likely much of his early life was spent upon the sea, sailing on the Mediterranean and along the west coast of Africa. Once he went as far north as England and perhaps even farther, but of this we are not certain.

2. READING: INFORMATIONAL TEXT

MULTIPLE CHOICE

8. **What is conflicting in the two sources regarding Columbus's birthday?** (RI.8.9)
    A. The first source is sure about his birthday, but the second source is unsure.
    B. The second source gives a different birthday year than the first source.
    C. The first source is unsure about his birthday, but the second source states this as a fact.
    D. The second source reveals that Columbus's birthday is actually years later than what was expected.

9. **In the first source, it states that Christopher Columbus grew up in a family that was not rich, but his father sent him away to school. What does this information imply since it somewhat contradicts what is in the second source?** (RI.8.9)
    A. Columbus was living in extreme poverty.
    B. Columbus's father probably borrowed money in order to send his son to school.
    C. Columbus grew up in a richer area and the sources are both wrong.
    D. Columbus was not very poor, but probably a little poorer than the middle class.

FREE RESPONSE

10. **Which source do you think is more reliable? Why?** (RL.8.9)

    _____

    _____

    _____

    _____

prepaze

2.3. INTEGRATION OF KNOWLEDGE AND IDEAS

2. READING: INFORMATIONAL TEXT

_____

_____

_____

_____

_____

_____

=== **FREE RESPONSE** ===

11.   What is a benefit to using print material when compared to audio text? (RI.8.7)

_____

_____

_____

_____

_____

_____

_____

_____

_____

_____

prepaze

2. READING: INFORMATIONAL TEXT

12. **The topic of a presentation includes how to install horizontal blinds in a room. Explain which medium would be best to use to relay the information.** (RI.8.7)

_____

_____

_____

_____

_____

_____

13. **If a source contains credible information, but also contains untrustworthy information, what should you do?** (RI.8.8, RI.8.9)

_____

_____

_____

_____

_____

_____

2.3. INTEGRATION OF KNOWLEDGE AND IDEAS

2. READING: INFORMATIONAL TEXT

_____

_____

14. **Explain how you can assess whether or not source evidence is relevant and credible.** (RI.8.8)

_____

_____

_____

_____

_____

_____

_____

_____

2.3. INTEGRATION OF KNOWLEDGE AND IDEAS

===== **TRUE OR FALSE** =====

15. **Graphic texts only include graphic organizers.** (RI.8.7)

    A. True   **B.** False

16. **A textbook is an example of a digital text.** (RI.8.7)

    A. True   **B.** False

17. **A multimedia presentation could include print text, images and other forms of mediums.** (RI.8.7)

    A. True   **B.** False

2. READING: INFORMATIONAL TEXT

18. **The credibility and authenticity of a source should always be considered when conducting research.** (RI.8.8)

    A. True   **B.** False

19. **All information is credible if it is located in a published document.** (RI.8.8)

    A. True   **B.** False

20. **TIf there is a discrepancy in the facts between two sources, you should not use either source.** (RI.8.9)

    A. True   **B.** False

2.4. CHAPTER REVIEW

2. READING: INFORMATIONAL TEXT

2.4. Chapter Review

> ➤ *Directions: Read the passage and answer the questions below.*

What's New in Home Tech

Almost everything today is digitally connected...whether at home or on the go. Connected technology saves you time with everything from smart phones to smart homes! Here's a look at some great smart tech that will help simplify your life.

First up...a laptop is a must! Made for today's mobile multitaskers, the thin and light Yoga C630 combines the power and productivity of a Windows 10 laptop with the always-on, always-connected mobility of a smartphone thanks to integrated 4G LTE and Wi-Fi support. It gets up to 22 hours of local video playback and features a natural pen-on paper experience on its vibrant 13.3-inch FHD IPS touchscreen display with optional Lenovo Pen and Windows Ink.

Next, to stay connected at home, Orbi Voice is a smart speaker integrated with Amazon voice assistant Alexa and uses the Qualcomm Wifi Mesh platform to create a complete whole home Wi Fi coverage with an entire ecosystem of other Wi-Fi products. It's truly an innovative leap, and the start of a trend expected to accelerate in the 5G era. Smart products can also help keep families safe. You can install Kidde Wire-Free Interconnect Smoke Alarms in your home. Kidde's new interconnect alarm solution offers exceptional safety benefits without the hassle of hardwiring or a Wi-Fi connection. The alarm also comes with a sealed 10-year battery; you don't have to worry about changing alarm batteries. Simply replace the entire alarm after 10 years.

Schlage Encode is the newest connected device to enhance the brand's portfolio of innovative smart locks. The deadbolt is easy to install, with a quick connection to in-home WiFi, making it even more convenient for homeowners to have secure, remote access control. Users can lock and unlock their deadbolt, monitor the lock's status, and send virtual keys to trusted friends and family from the convenience of their smartphone.

...continued next page

2. READING: INFORMATIONAL TEXT

This information, along with the lock's activity, can be tracked and monitored with an app, giving homeowners greater peace of mind. Through the Schlage Home app, users can also pair their deadbolt with Google Assistant and Amazon Alexa.

MULTIPLE CHOICE

1. **What is the purpose of this text?** (RI.8.6)
   A. The text is written is to persuade.
   B. The text is written to entertain.
   C. The text is written to inform.
   D. The text is written as a narrative story.

2. **What is the central idea of this text?** (RI.8.2)
   A. Modern homes can be equipped with electronics that can keep homeowners entertained and safe
   B. Electronic homes won't be developed until far into the future.
   C. Many tools can be purchased that will make life easy for elderly homeowners.
   D. A digitally connected home is what everybody wants nowadays.

3. **What idea keep repeating throughout the text, even though the author never states it directly?** (RI.8.2)
   A. Alexa is a great way to control various devices.
   B. A laptop is the best type of computer.
   C. It's important to have fun, but it's more important to be safe.
   D. Because all the devices have company names, they can be purchased.

prepaze

2. READING: INFORMATIONAL TEXT

4. **What does the Schlage Encode do?** (RI.8.1)

   A. It "can be tracked and monitored with an app."

   B. It allows users to "pair their deadbolt with Google Assistant and Amazon Alexa."

   C. It can "send virtual keys to trusted friends and family."

   D. All the above.

5. **Which of the following best describes the structure of this text?** (RI.8.5)

   A. Compare and contrast   **B.** Cause and effect

   C. Description   **D.** Sequence of events

> ➤ *Directions: Read the passage and answer the questions below.*

THE LOGIC OF VEGETARIANISM

Vegetarian: If you appeal to etymology, that raises another question altogether, and here, too, you will find the authorities against you. No one has a better right to speak on this matter than Professor J. E. B. Mayor, the great Latin scholar. He states that, according to word etymologically, "vegetarian" cannot mean "an eater of vegetables." It is derived from vegetus, or vigorous, and means "one who aims at vigour." I am not saying that the originators of the term "vegetarian" had this meaning in view, but merely that the etymological sense of the word does not favor your contention any more than the historical.

Verbalist: Well, what does "vegetarian" mean, then? How do you explain it yourself?

Vegetarian: A "vegetarian" is one who abstains from eating the flesh of animals, and whose food is mainly derived from the vegetable kingdom.

The above dialogue will show the absurdity and injustice of charging vegetarians, as the late Sir Henry Thompson did, with "equivocal terms, evasion—in short, untruthfulness," because they retain a title which was originally invented for their case. The statement that vegetarians have changed the meaning of their name is founded on similar ignorance of the facts. Here are two specimens of Sir Henry Thompson's inaccuracy. In 1885 he wrote:

...continued next page

2. READING: INFORMATIONAL TEXT

"It is high time that we should be spared the obscure language, or rather the inaccurate statement, to which milk and egg consumers are committed, in assuming a title which has for centuries belonged to that not inconsiderable body of persons whose habits of life confer the right to use it."

Observe that Sir Henry Thompson was then under the impression that the name "vegetarian" (invented in 1847) was "centuries" old! Nor, names apart, was he any more accurate in regards the practice itself. It can be proven on the authority of a long succession of writers, that the use of milk and its products is compatible with the Pythagorean or "vegetable" diet. The fact that some individual abstainers from meat have also abstained from all animal substances is no justification of this argument.

Thirteen years later Sir Henry Thompson's argument was entirely changed. His assertion of the history of the name "vegetarian" was quietly dropped. In fact, its novelty was now rather insisted on.

=== **MULTIPLE CHOICE** ===

6. **What is Salt's opinion of the dialogue included in the argument?** (RI.8.6, RI.8.8)

   A. He thinks it is ridiculous and unreasonable.

   B. He believes that verbalists have some accurate points in their argument.

   C. He thinks that vegetarians should listen to verbalists.

   D. This dialogue offers a good source of reasoning for both sides of the argument.

7. **What was Sir Thompson's initial argument regarding vegetarianism?** (RI.8.1)

   A. People should not become vegetarians because they should support farmers.

   B. The meaning of the term "vegetarian" has been changed from its original meaning.

   C. Vegetarians consume eggs, milk, and other animal products.

   D. Vegetarianism is a passing phase.

2.4. CHAPTER REVIEW

2. READING: INFORMATIONAL TEXT

2. 4. CHAPTER REVIEW

8. **How does Salt explain vegetarians who do not eat animal products in their diet?** (RI.8.1)

    A. The term "vegetarian" still includes both them and those who eat non-flesh animal products.

    B. These vegetarians are making a poor choice for themselves.

    C. Those who refuse to eat animal products as part of their diet are not vegetarians.

    D. Animal products most likely are not found in the urban areas near their residence.

> ➤ *Directions: Read the passage and answer the questions below.*

THE WHITE HOUSE COOKBOOK

The usual custom among professional cooks is to entirely immerse the food item in boiling fat, but from inconvenience most households use the half-frying method. This consists of frying food in a small amount of fat in a frying pan. For the first method, a shallow iron frying kettle is best to use. The fat should half fill the kettle and be sufficient enough to float whatever is to be fried. The heat of the fat should get to such a degree that when a piece of bread or a teaspoonful of the batter is dropped in it, it will become brown almost instantly. However, the temperature should not be so hot as to burn the fat. Some cooks say that the fat should be smoking, but my experience is that this ruins the fat. As soon as it begins to smoke it should be removed a little to one side, and still be kept at the boiling point. If fritters, crullers, croquettes, etc., are dropped into fat that is too hot, it crusts over the outside before the inside has fully risen. This creates a heavy, hard article and gives the fat a burnt flavor.

=== **MULTIPLE CHOICE** ===

9. **When the author makes reference to the "heavy, hard article," what is she referring to?** (RI.8.4)

    A. The equipment needed to fry food

    B. The finished cooking product

    C. The amount of oil needed to fry food

    D. The recipe from the cookbook

2. READING: INFORMATIONAL TEXT

10. **What does the word *immerse* mean?** (RI.8.4)

The usual custom among professional cooks is to entirely <u>immerse</u> the food item in boiling fat, but from inconvenience most households use the half-frying method.

A. Submerge deeply into a liquid
B. Place into a shallow amount of liquid
C. Remove from a container filled with liquid
D. Avoid contact with the liquid

11. **How does the author justify avoiding fat smoke when frying it?** (RI.8.6)

A. She bases this information on her own experience.
B. She explains how it is simply wrong.
C. She provides documentation from French chefs.
D. She shows data on how fat is burned when it smokes.

> ➤ *Directions: Read the passage and answer the questions below.*

Apples come in a variety of colors and flavors. Colors can range from bright yellow to dark red. Apples can be sweet, tart or even bitter in taste. Golden Delicious apples are yellow with an intensely sweet flavor. Red Delicious apples, contrarily, are not very flavorful. Granny Smith apples are green and tangy, making them a perfect ingredient for delicious pies. Some multi-colored apples include Fiji, Honeycrisp, and Cortland. Although apples may appear to be quite different, they all belong to the same classification of fruits. Apples are true wonders of nature.

2.4. CHAPTER REVIEW

=== **MULTIPLE CHOICE** ===

12. **What is the central idea of this passage?** (RI.8.2)

A. Red Delicious apples, on the other hand, are not very flavorful.
B. Apples can be used to make pies.
C. Golden Delicious apples are yellow with an intensely sweet flavor.
D. Apples come in a variety of colors and flavors.

prepaze

2. READING: INFORMATIONAL TEXT

13. **Which sentence best supports the central idea of this passage?** (RI.8.2)
    A. Colors can range from bright yellow to dark red.
    B. Apples are true wonders of nature.
    C. Some people do not like to eat apples.
    D. Apples grow on trees.

14. **Which sentence does NOT support the central idea of this passage?** (RI.8.2)
    A. Some multi-colored apples include Fiji, Honeycrisp, and Cortland.
    B. Granny Smith apples are green and tangy, making them a perfect fit for delicious pies
    C. Apples are very healthy.
    D. Apples can be sweet, tart or even bitter in taste.

15. **Which sentence could also describe the central idea of this passage?** (RI.8.2)
    A. Apples are my favorite fruit.
    B. Apples can vary in appearance and taste.
    C. Gala apples are red.
    D. Many people like to visit apple orchards.

> ➤ *Directions: Read the passage and answer the questions below.*

Facts About Frogs

Amphibians constitute two very easily recognized sub-divisions,--the one including the Frogs and Toads, collectively forming the Tailless group; and the other represented by the Newts and Salamanders, or Tailed Amphibians. The former group has an almost world-wide distribution, numbering more than 6400 species; it is most abundantly represented in the tropics, ranging in diminishing numbers to the limits of the Arctic Circle.

...continued next page

prepaze   **www.prepaze.com**

2. READING: INFORMATIONAL TEXT

In colder climates these animals usually hibernate during the winter months; while in tropical countries, where dry seasons intervene, they often bury themselves in the mud, and remain in a state of suspended animation till the return of the rains. The majority are more or less essentially nocturnal in their habits. Frogs and toads commence life as aquatic tadpoles. While in the adult state they are generally carnivorous , even cannibalistic, the tadpoles are vegetarian feeders. The loudest-voiced member of this group is the bullfrog of Canada and the United States. The length of the body in this species may be as much as 7½ inches, excluding the legs; its croakings are so loud that they may be heard for a distance of several miles. These sounds are most pronounced during the early spring or breeding season. In the Southern United States, however, they are maintained more or less persistently throughout the year.

2.4. CHAPTER REVIEW

=══════════ **FILL IN THE BLANK** ══════════=

16. **The purpose of the text is to** _____ **readers about frogs and toads.** (RI.8.6)

17. **Paragraph 1 explains the** _____ **between two types of amphibians.**
(RI.8.5)

18. **Paragraph 2** _____ **bullfrogs and other frogs based on characteristics such as size and sound.** (RI.8.3, RI.8.5)

19. **According to Paragraph 2, newts and salamanders have** _____ **, while frogs and toads have** _____ **.** (RI.8.3, RI.8.5)

2. READING: INFORMATIONAL TEXT

═══ FREE RESPONSE ═══

20. Explain how each paragraph helps to develop the key concept of the text.

_____

_____

_____

_____

_____

_____

_____

_____

_____

_____

_____

_____

_____

_____

2. 4. CHAPTER REVIEW

2. READING: INFORMATIONAL TEXT

> *Directions: Read the passages and answer the questions below.*

THE LIFE OF CHRISTOPHER COLUMBUS

It is easy now to see and to say that Columbus himself was singularly well fitted to take the charge of the expedition of discovery. He was an excellent sailor and at the same time he was a learned geographer and a good mathematician. He was living in Portugal, the kings of which country had, for many years, fostered the exploration of the coast of Africa, and were pushing expeditions farther and farther South.

AMERICAN LEADERS AND HEROES

In the course of many voyages he heard much of the work done by Portuguese sailors and discoverers, for Portugal was at that time one of the greatest sea-powers of the world. As Lisbon, the capital of Portugal, was naturally a centre for sea-faring men, and as it was also the home of his brother Bartholomew, Columbus, at the age of about thirty-five, went there to live.

Columbus was a man of commanding presence. He was large, tall, and dignified in bearing, with a ruddy complexion and piercing blue-gray eyes. By the time he was thirty his hair had become white, and fell in wavy locks about his shoulders. Although his life of hardship and poverty compelled him to be plain and simple in food and dress, he always had the air of a gentleman, and his manners were pleasing and courteous. But he had a strong will, which overcame difficulties that would have overwhelmed most men.

═══════════ **TRUE OR FALSE** ═══════════

21. **In both sources, Christopher Columbus' characteristics are depicted in a positive nature.** (RI.8.9)

    A. True　　　　　　　　　**B.** False

22. **According to the second source, Columbus was more likely to become a wool preparer like his father.** (RI.8.9)

    A. True　　　　　　　　　**B.** False

2. READING: INFORMATIONAL TEXT

23. **The first source implies that Columbus was an inherent, or natural-born, sailor and adventurer.** (RI.8.9)

   A. True   **B.** False

> ➤ *Directions: Read the questions and select the best answer choice.*

=== **MULTIPLE CHOICE** ===

24. **A math student must research the origin of the Pythagorean Theorem. She finds two different print books from the reference center at the library. The information in each book contradicts one another. What should the student do?** (RI.8.9)

   A. Inform the librarian that the books contain false information.

   B. Find more resources to further investigate the topic.

   C. Put these two books back and start the research over.

   D. Pick the books that seem to have more information in it.

25. **Which type of medium would allow the audience to authentically experience a historical time period?** (RI.8.7)

   A. Print text   **B.** Graphic text

   C. Video production   **D.** Audio production

26. **What is or are the benefit(s) of watching to a video of a speech as opposed to reading it?** (RI.8.7)

   A. The tone expressed by the speaker would help the audience to understand the message.

   B. Seeing the actual speaker allows the audience to interpret their body language and gestures.

   C. The audience can see the reactions of the crowd listening to the speech.

   D. All of the above

2. 4. CHAPTER REVIEW

2. READING: INFORMATIONAL TEXT

=== **FREE RESPONSE** ===

27. **You are given a printed version of a presentation that took place yesterday. Why are you at a disadvantage compared to those who witnessed the presentation in person?** (RI.8.7)

_____

_____

_____

_____

_____

_____

_____

_____

_____

_____

28. **What are the benefits of presenting information with an image instead of a text?** (RI.8.7)

_____

_____

_____

_____

2.4. CHAPTER REVIEW

prepaze

2. READING: INFORMATIONAL TEXT

_____

_____

_____

_____

_____

_____

_____

29. **Sarah is conducting research about the ways in which pollution issues are resolved in other countries. She wants her essay to be accurate with direct evidence. How can she make sure that her essay is reliable and credible?** (RI.8.8)

_____

_____

_____

_____

_____

_____

_____

_____

2. READING: INFORMATIONAL TEXT

_____

_____

_____

_____

30. **If you refer to multiple sources, but they all contain conflicting information with each other, what does this most likely mean?** (RI.8.9)

_____

_____

_____

_____

_____

_____

_____

_____

_____

_____

_____

_____

prepaze

3. WRITING

3. WRITING

~~~ 3.1. Text Types and Purposes ~~~

Common Core State Standards: CCSS.ELA-LITERACY.W.8.1, CCSS.ELA-LITERACY.W.8.2, CCSS.ELA-LITERACY.W.8.3

Skills:

- Write arguments to support claims with clear reasons and relevant evidence.
- Write informative/explanatory texts to examine a topic and convey ideas, concepts, and information.
- Write narratives to develop real or imagined experiences or events using an effective technique.

=== **EXAMPLE** ===

E1 **Which of the following would be an appropriate thesis statement for the following prompt?** (W.8.1)

Prompt: Write about a personal characteristic that you think is valuable.

- **A.** Hunger is a serious issue because food is very important to everyone.
- **B.** The most valued characteristic is either honesty or a good sense of humor.
- **C.** Everyone should be funny because laughter is the best medicine.
- **D.** The most valued characteristic is generosity because we should help those who are in need.

Answer: **D.** This thesis statement best addresses the prompt and summarizes the main argument of the essay.

3. WRITING

E2 **Which of the following would best fit an informative essay about extreme sports?** (W.8.2)

   A. The most important extreme sport is cliff jumping.

   B. Extreme sports should only be played by professional daredevils.

   C. Extreme sports usually include towering heights or fast speeds.

   D. It is best to stay away from extreme sports due to the dangers they present.

Answer: **C.** This statement is a fact that can be proven. Informative writing should include concrete facts and details.

E3 **How could you strengthen the following sentence from a narrative story?**

Caroline hummed as she brushed her hair.

Answer: The sentence can be strengthened by using more descriptive language. Ex.: Caroline hummed a delightful tune as she brushed her long, brown hair.

➤ *Directions: Read the question and select the best answer choice.*

══════════════ **MULTIPLE CHOICE** ══════════════

1. **Bonnie is writing an opinion piece about the best hairstyles for teen girls. Her argument is that long curls is the most popular trend. How can Bonnie include a counterclaim in her argument while also supporting her own her claim?** (W.8.1)

   A. She can give her opinion about why the short haircut is unstylish.

   B. She can provide evidence of the number of teens who do not like short haircuts.

   C. She could cite a positive opinion about short haircuts, and refute it with an explanation of reasons why some dislike short haircuts.

   D. She should leave the counterclaim out of her argument in order to avoid confusion.

3.1. TEXT TYPES AND PURPOSES

3. WRITING

2. **Taylor is writing an argument against camping trips. She includes statistical evidence as well as logical reasons in her essay. How do both of these strategies support her claim?** (w.8.1)

A. They both visually convey Taylor's message to the reader.

B. They both let the reader know how important camping is.

C. They both provide the reader with facts as well as a clearly developed opinion about camping.

D. They both support the counterclaim that camping is important and should be experienced by everyone.

3. **Which phrase would a writer most likely use when stating his or her claim?** (w.8.1)

A. "In other words"   **B.** "In contrast"

C. "In my opinion"   **D.** "In conclusion"

4. **Which topic would be the most appropriate for an informative essay?** (w.8.2)

A. The top 3 best brands of cereal

B. Why horses gallop

C. My life on the horse farm

D. The cell phone company everyone should use

5. **Which of the following would NOT be relevant to the following prompt:** (w.8.2)

Write about cell phone usage in third world countries.

A. Information about solar power in third world countries

B. Information about cell phone carriers located in third world countries

C. Information about the increased need for cell phones in third world countries

D. Information about a recent increase in technology usage in third world countries

3. WRITING

6. **Which of the following details would best support an article about an increase in crime?** (W.8.2)

   A. Most crimes are committed in large cities.

   B. Violent crimes include harming someone.

   C. Overcrowded prisons have caused guard dissatisfaction.

   D. A rise in crime may be the result of poor education.

7. **You want to introduce your characters appropriately in a story. Which of the following statements below would work best?** (W.8.3)

   A. Incredible would describe Sally as she came through the front door.

   B. Walking through the door, Sally was incredible.

   C. Sally looked incredible as she walked through the door.

   D. Incredibly, Sally walked through the door.

8. **Which sentence best illustrates an event in the story?** (W.8.3)

   A. Chef Misty kneaded the dough strenuously, with all of her might.

   B. Misty was the most talented chef of the restaurant.

   C. Misty is ecstatic because she is a chef who is kneading the dough.

   D. Chef Misty is a chef who kneads the dough.

9. **What is the function of a story's conclusion?** (W.8.3)

   A. It shows the main character's behavior.

   B. It introduces the conflict.

   C. It presents a problem in the story.

   D. It reflects on past events from the story.

=== **TRUE OR FALSE?** ===

10. **Sarah is writing an argumentative essay about the dangers of skateboarding. An interview with a famous skateboarder would not be a credible source of evidence.** (W.8.1)

    A. True   **B.** False

prepaze

3.1. TEXT TYPES AND PURPOSES

3. WRITING

11. **Mary is writing an argumentative essay about the importance of having cell phones. She should exclusively include facts about cell phones as evidence to support her claim.** (W.8.1)

    A. True   **B.** False

12. **Writers should include definitions of key terms in an informative essay.** (W.8.2)

    A. True   **B.** False

13. **If a student writes the exact words from a source without giving credit to the author, he or she would be committing plagiarism.** (W.8.2)

    A. True   **B.** False

14. **A flashback is a narrative technique that introduces events that happened before the beginning of the story.** (W.8.3)

    A. True   **B.** False

15. **Technical vocabulary is not an effective technique in narrative development.** (W.8.3)

    A. True   **B.** False

=== **FREE RESPONSE** ===

16. **Lyla uses random, unverified websites to find evidence for her argumentative essay. In what way could these sources impact her argumentative essay?** (W.8.1)

    _____

    _____

    _____

    _____

    _____

prepaze   **www.prepaze.com**

3. WRITING

_____

_____

_____

_____

_____

_____

_____

17. Karen's informative essay involves Einstein's theory of relativity. How could Karen incorporate domain-specific vocabulary into her informative essay? (W.8.2)

_____

_____

_____

_____

_____

_____

_____

_____

_____

prepaze

3. WRITING

_____

_____

_____

18. **Hannah is writing a short story, but she is in a hurry. She does not consider pacing in her writing. How could this impact the development of her story?** (W.8.3)

_____

_____

_____

_____

_____

_____

_____

_____

_____

_____

_____

3. WRITING

19. Write an introductory paragraph to support the following claim: (W.8.1)

Students should be allowed to participate in at least 1 hour of recess per day.

_____

_____

_____

_____

_____

_____

_____

_____

_____

_____

_____

_____

_____

_____

_____

3.1. TEXT TYPES AND PURPOSES

3. WRITING

20. Write a conclusion for the following narrative events: (W.8.3)

He feared that they would be violently smacked into the sea. The long journey had been plagued by vicious winds and turbulence. The pilot was burdened by the thought of risking the lives of passengers, but he was confident in his sense of direction. He knew what he had to do. As he prepared for the announcement, he let out of deep breath.

_____

_____

_____

_____

_____

_____

_____

_____

_____

_____

3.1. TEXT TYPES AND PURPOSES

3.2. PRODUCTION AND DISTRIBUTION OF WRITING

3. WRITING

～ 3.2. Production and Distribution of Writing ～

Common Core State Standards: CCSS.ELA-LITERACY.W.8.4, CCSS.ELA-LITERACY.W.8.5

Skills:

- Produce clear and coherent writing in which the development, organization, and style are appropriate to task, purpose, and audience.
- With some guidance and support from peers and adults, develop and strengthen writing as needed by planning, revising, editing, rewriting.

=== **EXAMPLE** ===

E1 **The teacher asks you to write about a time in your life when you made a mistake but corrected it. In what style of writing does the teacher expect you to write?** (W.8.4)

  A. Compare and contrast

  B. Informative

  C. Narrative

  D. Argumentative

Answer: **C.** Since the teacher is asking you to describe a personal experience, it would most likely be written in a narrative format.

E2 **Why is it important to edit and revise your writing?** (W.8.5)

  A. To check for grammatical and spelling errors

  B. To rewrite poorly developed material

  C. To add new words, phrases, and sentences

  D. All of the above

Answer: **D.** Editing and revising are an important part of the writing process for all of these reasons.

3.2. PRODUCTION AND DISTRIBUTION OF WRITING

3. WRITING

> ➤ *Directions: Read the questions and select the best answer choice.*

=== **MULTIPLE CHOICE** ===

1. **When introducing a writing assignment to students, what information should teachers provide first?** (W.8.4)

    A. Format   **B.** Development   **C.** Organization   **D.** Task

2. **Karen has written her essay. She proofreads it and notices that it is not properly organized. What is most likely true about Karen's essay?** (W.8.4)

    A. The essay does not address the intended purpose.
    B. The essay task is incomplete.
    C. The essay would not clearly convey Karen's ideas.
    D. The essay would lack credible evidence.

3. **The teacher asks the class to write about the following topic. What is the purpose of this writing task?** (W.8.4)

    Prompt: In what way was the Battle of Saratoga the turning point in the American Revolutionary War?

    A. To explain, in a series of steps, the details of the battle.
    B. To inform the reader about how these events are connected.
    C. To entertain the reader with a story with a background of the American Revolutionary War.
    D. To persuade the reader to believe that this battle was the most important battle of the war.

4. **Betty has just finished her argumentative essay and needs a peer to proofread her essay. Who would be the best person to help Betty?** (W.8.5)

    A. A friend who agrees with her topic.
    B. A new classmate that she does not know well.
    C. A classmate with an unbiased view on the topic.
    D. None of the above

3. WRITING

5. **While editing her informative essay, Sarah realizes that her wording was repetitive throughout. However, Sarah's teacher required a 500-word essay. At this point, Sarah has just enough words to satisfy the requirement. What should she do?** (W.8.5)

   A. Replace certain words with synonyms.

   B. Remove the sentences with repetitive words and write new sentences.

   C. Start the essay over and rewrite it.

   D. Remove the repetitive words and turn it in without having 500 words.

6. **Carol wrote a short story about a fairy that lives in a faraway land. Carol's assignment was to write a short historical fiction story. What is wrong with Carol's writing assignment?** (W.8.5)

   A. The audience does not match to the writing assignment.

   B. The purpose and task were not addressed.

   C. The story is about a fairy instead of multiple characters.

   D. The plot and setting of the story are wrong.

   ===== **FILL IN THE BLANK** =====

7. **The main purpose for writing about the life cycles of frogs and toads would be to _____ the audience.** (W.8.4)

8. **Robin's teacher asks the class to write about their favorite time to study. Robin writes about her favorite subject to study. She did not address the appropriate_____.** (W.8.4)

9. **As Sarah organizes her informative essay about British soldiers, she will include an introduction, body paragraphs and a**

   _____. (W.8.4)

10. **Pete is writing an essay. He could use a/an _____ to help structure his ideas before he begins writing.** (W.8.5)

3. WRITING

11. **Jake is writing an article about toys that should be recalled due to child injuries. This article's intended** _____ **is parents and teachers.** (W.8.5)

12. **In Sarah's narrative writing, she uses** _____ **words/phrases to show the relationships among experiences and events.** (W.8.5)

=== **TRUE OR FALSE** ===

13. **It is not necessary to consider the audience of a writing task until after the first draft is complete.** (W.8.4)

    A. True   **B.** False

14. **The teacher informs a student that she wrote a narrative instead of a descriptive essay. This means that the student wrote her assignment in the wrong style.** (W.8.4)

    A. True   **B.** False

15. **During the revision step in the writing process, Kevin should check his writing for grammatical and spelling mistakes.** (W.8.5)

    A. True   **B.** False

16. **Kelly is asked to write about an event during the American Civil War. She should first conduct research in order to decide which topic to write about.** (W.8.5)

    A. True   **B.** False

3. WRITING

17. **What would be the purpose and style of an essay about how candy is made in a factory?** (W.8.4)

_____

_____

_____

_____

_____

_____

_____

_____

_____

_____

18. **What is the relationship between the purpose and style of a piece of writing?** (W.8.4)

_____

_____

_____

_____

_____

3.2. PRODUCTION AND DISTRIBUTION OF WRITING

prepaze

3. WRITING

_____

_____

_____

_____

_____

19. **While proofreading her own essay, Tiffany finds that her ideas do not support her claim during her revision process. Explain what she should do.** (W.8.5)

_____

_____

_____

_____

_____

_____

_____

_____

_____

_____

3. WRITING

20. **George has written in an informative essay about a historical figure. His conclusion is simply the introduction rewritten in different words. How can George strengthen his conclusion?** (W.8.5)

_____

_____

_____

_____

_____

_____

_____

_____

_____

_____

3.3. CHAPTER REVIEW

3. WRITING

~ 3.3. Chapter Review ~

> ➤ Directions: *Read the questions and select the best answer choice.*

═ MULTIPLE CHOICE ═

1. **Cara is writing an argumentative essay. How does this style affect the purpose of the essay?** (W.8.1)
   A. It provides the format for writing her essay in a persuasive way.
   B. It provides the format for writing her essay in an explanatory way.
   C. It enables the writer to use narrative techniques.
   D. It allows the writer to complete the assignment.

2. **The teacher asks the class to write an argumentative essay about the best game show on television. What evidence below would support the topic?** (W.8.1)
   A. Factual information from an encyclopedia about game shows
   B. A list of the different games shows that are on television
   C. An interview with a game show host who knows many facts
   D. Results from a survey conducted about popular game shows

3. **Which of the following narrative techniques is shown in the example below?** (W.8.3)

   "Quiet, everyone. The baby is sleeping," the mother whispered.

   "How long will the baby sleep?" the babysitter asked.

   "Oh, for about 2 hours," the mother replied.

   A. Flashback   B. Foreshadowing
   C. Dialogue   D. Description

3. WRITING

4. **Beth's informative essay about community crisis resources includes quotes from community leaders. How will these quotes help support the information in her informative essay?** (W.8.2)

   A. It will provide a firsthand account of the support given during a crisis.

   B. It will help to summarize Beth's thesis statement.

   C. It will allow the reader to experience Beth's personal experiences.

   D. Beth should not use quotes in this type of writing.

5. **A peer edit is completed by one of your classmates. She tells you that your writing piece does not fit the purpose of the prompt. What should you do?** (W.8.4)

   A. Rewrite the two weakest paragraphs so that they answer the prompt.

   B. Rewrite the introduction and conclusion paragraphs.

   C. Add a few lines that pertain to the prompt.

   D. Start over so that it completely pertains to the prompt.

6. **Molly must select a topic from a list in order to write her informative essay. Which topic should Molly choose?** (W.8.5)

   A. A topic that she is familiar with

   B. A topic that she is somewhat familiar with

   C. A topic that she has never heard of

   D. A topic that her friend is also writing about

prepaze

3. WRITING

7. **You are assigned the following writing assignment by your teacher. Which statement depicts what you should do after reading the prompt?** (W.8.4)

   Assignment: Research studies have concluded that the driver's license age requirement should be raised to 18 in all states due to the significant number of teenage crashes in the past few decades. Write a persuasive essay about whether the age requirement of 18 should be enforced immediately.

   A. Prepare to explain both sides without having a definitive opinion.
   B. Take a clear stance on the issue and back it with supporting evidence.
   C. Pick a side and stick with it but express that you don't fully agree with this side.
   D. Do not take a side at all.

8. **Which of the following transition words or phrases would best link these two sentences together?** (W.8.2)

   Fire can quickly erupt, causing extensive destruction. Earthquakes can result in severe property damage.

   A. In addition to
   B. Also
   C. On the other hand
   D. In conclusion

9. **Mary wants to write a narrative in the form of a short story. How should she begin?** (W.8.3)

   A. Describe all of the settings that will be used in the story.
   B. Use dialogue between the characters in the story.
   C. Introduce the characters through descriptions and events.
   D. Introducing the conflict with falling action.

3. WRITING

10. **Samantha is gathering her sources for her argumentative essay about the most dangerous occupation in the world. Which source would be the most beneficial to use?** (W.8.1)

   A. Internet website on jobs worldwide

   B. Her opinion and her family's opinion on their job experiences

   C. Statistics from an international health organization on job-related injuries

   D. A quote from a football player about job-related injuries and his experiences

═══════════════ **FILL IN THE BLANK** ═══════════════

11. **An unverified website about the Civil War may not be a _____ source of evidence.** (W.8.1)

12. **Michael writes an essay about how to cook fish on a camping stove. This is an example of _____ writing.** (W.8.2)

13. **A good narrative should reveal the thoughts, feelings and actions of the _____ throughout the text.** (W.8.3)

14. **A diary entry is an example of personal _____ writing.** (W.8.4)

15. **A writing prompt describes the task and _____ of an assignment.** (W.8.5)

3.3. CHAPTER REVIEW

3. WRITING

=== **FREE RESPONSE** ===

16. **In order to support your claim against eating healthier meals at lunch, you write the following statement: There are about 575 calories in the average lunch. How can you use this statement as evidence?** (W.8.1)

_____

_____

_____

_____

_____

_____

_____

_____

17. **Patricia's is writing an essay about the economy. She includes definitions of economic terms such as tariff and exports. How will this help to develop her topic?** (W.8.2)

_____

_____

_____

_____

3. WRITING

_____

_____

_____

_____

_____

_____

18. How do transition words help to develop events in the following story? (W.8.3)

Ben first called his friend to see if he could come over. Then, he quickly cleaned his room. Soon after, Joshua arrived as he was eager to play the new video game.

_____

_____

_____

_____

_____

_____

_____

_____

prepaze

3. WRITING

19. **A teacher asks his students to write about the most influential person in the world. How could this be written in several structures and styles?** (W.8.4)

_____

_____

_____

_____

_____

_____

_____

_____

20. **After you proofread and revise and edit your essay, you need to rewrite your essay in a final draft. Explain why this is necessary.** (W.8.5)

_____

_____

_____

_____

_____

3. WRITING

_____

_____

_____

_____

_____

_____

_____

TRUE OR FALSE

21. **Lyle claims that forensic science should be used to solve crimes. In his writing, he should state his opinion directly.** (W.8.1)

    A. True   **B.** False

22. **An informative essay about restaurants should include the writer's opinion and personal experiences.** (W.8.2)

    A. True   **B.** False

23. **Ms. Thompson assigns her 8th-grade class to write a narrative. This means that the students can only write about imaginary events.** (W.8.3)

    A. True   **B.** False

24. **A persuasive essay about traffic safety could include statistics about the number of recent car crashes.** (W.8.4)

    A. True   **B.** False

25. **During the writing process, it is important to plan and organize your ideas before you begin writing.** (W.8.5)

    A. True   **B.** False

3. WRITING

=== **WRITING PROMPT** ===

26. Write an introductory paragraph to support the following claim. (W.8.1)

Students should not have to attend summer classes.

_____

_____

_____

_____

_____

_____

_____

_____

_____

_____

_____

_____

_____

_____

3. WRITING

27. Use transition words to rewrite the following text. (W.8.2, W.8.5)

The key to proper oral care is to follow a daily regimen. Carefully floss your teeth to remove any food residue. Brush your teeth with a fluoride toothpaste. Use mouthwash to gargle and rinse for fresh, healthy breath.

_____

_____

_____

_____

_____

_____

_____

_____

_____

_____

_____

_____

_____

_____

3.3. CHAPTER REVIEW

 prepaze

3. WRITING

28. Write a dialogue between the characters below in a narrative text. (W.8.3)

Harold walked into Principal Morris' office reluctantly. He knew that the prank had landed him in big trouble. Principal Morris was surely expecting a full explanation.

_____

_____

_____

_____

_____

_____

_____

_____

_____

_____

_____

_____

_____

3. WRITING

29. Write a brief counterargument for the following claim. (W.8.1)

The driver's license age requirement should be raised to 18 in all states. This is due to the significant number of teenage crashes in the past few decades.

_____

_____

_____

_____

_____

_____

_____

_____

_____

_____

_____

_____

_____

_____

3. WRITING

30. Write an informative essay about a topic related to offshore oil drilling. (W.8.2)

_____

_____

_____

_____

_____

_____

_____

_____

_____

_____

_____

_____

_____

_____

_____

3. WRITING

prepaze

4. LANGUAGE

4. LANGUAGE

～～ 4.1. Vocabulary Acquisition and Use ～～

Common Core State Standards: CCSS.ELA-LITERACY.L.8.4, CCSS.ELA-LITERACY.L.8.5

Skills:

- Determine or clarify the meaning of unknown and multiple-meaning words or phrases.
- Demonstrate an understanding of figurative language and word relationships.

➢ *Directions: Read the passage and answer the questions below.*

━━━━━ **EXAMPLE** ━━━━━

CALL OF THE WILD

There he lay for the remainder of the weary night, nursing his wrath and wounded pride. He could not understand what it all meant. What did they want with him, these strange men? Why were they keeping him pent up in this narrow crate? He did not know why, but he felt oppressed by the vague sense of impending calamity. Several times during the night he sprang to his feet when the shed door rattled open, expecting to see the Judge or the boys at least. But each time it was the bulging face of the saloon-keeper that peered in at him by the sickly light of a tallow candle. And each time the joyful bark that trembled in Buck's throat was twisted into a savage growl.

E1   What does the word *oppressed* mean in this sentence? (L.8.4)

He did not know why, but he felt <u>oppressed</u> by the vague sense of impending calamity.

A. Enthusiastic   **B.** Surprised   **C.** Worried   **D.** Hungry

Answer: C. He was worried that being confined in a cage meant something bad, a calamity, was impending, or about to happen.

4. LANGUAGE

E2 **Which phrase helps to identify the meaning of *oppressed*?** (L.8.5)

    A. "began a passage through many hands"

    B. "the vague sense of impending calamity"

    C. "in the morning four men entered"

    D. "with an assortment of boxes and parcels"

Answer: **B.** The idea of being "oppressed" is one of being treated badly or kept confined. The "vague sense" is feeling and being confined made him feel worried and bad.

> *Directions: Read the passage and answer the questions below.*

4.1. VOCABULARY ACQUISITION AND USE

THE INVISIBLE LIBRARY

She quickly trotted back down the corridor to the trophy room, and pushed the door open. The light from the corridor gleamed on the silver cups and glass display cabinets. Without bothering to kindle the room's central lantern, she crossed to the second cupboard on the right. She could still smell the polish she'd used on the wood two days ago. Opening its door, she withdrew the pile of books stacked at the back, and pulled out a battered volume in dark purple leather.

(When Pestifer sent the book to the school, had he fretted and paced the floor, hoping to get some sort of acknowledgement back from the teachers, praising his research, wishing him future success? Or had they sent him a bare form letter to say that they'd received it – and then dropped his work into a pile of other self-published vanity books sent by ex-pupils and forgotten all about it?)

Fortunately it was a fairly small volume. She tucked it into a hidden pocket, returned the other books to cover her tracks, and then hesitated.

This was, after all, a school that taught magic. And as a Librarian she had one big advantage that nobody else had – not necromancers, Fae, dragons, ordinary humans or anyone. It was called the Language. Only Librarians could read it. Only Librarians could use it. It could affect certain aspects of reality. It was extremely useful, even if the vocabulary needed constant revision. Unfortunately, it didn't work on pure magic. If the masters at the school had set some sort of alarm spell to prevent anyone stealing the cups, and if that worked on anything that was

...continued next page

4. LANGUAGE

taken out of the room, then she might be in for a nasty surprise. And it would be hideously embarrassing to be hunted down by a mob of teenagers.

Irene mentally shook herself. She'd planned for this. There was no point in delaying any longer, and standing around reconsidering possibilities would only result in her running short on time. She stepped across the threshold.

Sudden raucous noise broke the silence. The stone arch above the doorway rippled, lips forming from the stone to howl, "Thief! Thief!"

=== **MULTIPLE CHOICE** ===

1. **What is the meaning of the word *gleamed*?** (L.8.4)

    The light from the corridor <u>gleamed</u> on the silver cups and glass display cabinets.

    A. Lost   **B.** Shone   **C.** Caught   **D.** Laughed

2. **Which word(s) or phrases help to identify the meaning of *gleamed* in the text?** (L.8.4, L.8.5)

    A. Silver cups   **B.** Glass display cabinets
    C. The light from the corridor   **D.** Trophy

3. **What is the meaning of the word *fretted*?** (L.8.4)

    A. Danced   **B.** Frowned   **C.** Cooked   **D.** Worried

4. **Which word(s) or phrases help to identify the meaning of *fretted* in the text?** (L.8.4, L.8.5)

    A. Paced the floor   **B.** Praising his research
    C. Acknowledgement   **D.** Future Success

4.1. VOCABULARY ACQUISITION AND USE

4. LANGUAGE

5. **The Latin prefix re- means "again." What is the meaning of the word *revision?*** (L.8.4)

It was extremely useful, even if the vocabulary needed constant revision.

A. Cleaning   **B.** Correction   **C.** Emotion   **D.** Belonging

6. **Which dictionary definition best fits the context of the underlined word?** (L.8.4)

Sudden <u>raucous</u> noise broke the silence.

A. Extremely rough or grating   **B.** Rowdy and disorderly
C. Disturbingly harsh and loud   **D.** None of the above

> *Directions: Read the passage and answer the questions below.*

FAHRENHEIT 451

    With his symbolic helmet numbered 451 on his stolid head, and his eyes all orange flame with the thought of what came next, he flicked the igniter and the house jumped up in a gorging fire that burned the evening sky red and yellow and black. He strode in a swarm of fireflies.

    He wanted above all, like the old joke, to shove a marshmallow on a stick in the furnace, while the flapping pigeon-winged books died on the porch and lawn of the house. While the books went up in sparkling whirls and blew away on a wind turned dark with burning. Montag grinned the fierce grin of all men singed and driven back by flame. He knew that when he returned to the firehouse, he might wink at himself, a minstrel man, burnt-corked, in the mirror. Later, going to sleep, he would feel the fiery smile still gripped by his face muscles, in the dark. It never went away. That smile, it never ever went away as long as he remembered.

4.1. VOCABULARY ACQUISITION AND USE

4. LANGUAGE

=== **MULTIPLE CHOICE** ===

7.   What is the literal meaning of the underlined phrase? (L.8.5)

... he flicked the igniter and <u>the house jumped up in a gorging fire</u> that burned the evening sky red and yellow and black.

A. The house split open into a wide gorge.
B. The house grew legs and jumped in the air.
C. The firefighter jumped on top of the house.
D. The house burst into flames.

8.   Which of the following best describes the figurative language used in the above phrase? (L.8.5)

A. Personification   **B.** Alliteration
C. Simile   **D.** Onomatopoeia

9.   What is the literal meaning of the underlined phrase? (L.8.5)

He wanted above all, like the old joke, to shove a marshmallow on a stick in the furnace, while <u>the flapping pigeon-winged books died on the porch</u> and lawn of the house.

A. The birds were hurt on the porch.
B. The pigeon-winged books had been alive.
C. The book pages flapped like wings in the fire.
D. The books stopped breathing.

10.   Which of the following best describes the figurative language used in the above sentence? (L.8.5)

A. Hyperbole   **B.** Metaphor
C. Irony   **D.** Personification

4. LANGUAGE

> **Directions:** *Read the poem and answer the questions below.*

I WANDERED LONELY AS A CLOUD

I wandered lonely as a cloud
That floats on high o'er vales and hills,
When all at once I saw a crowd,
A host, of golden daffodils;
Beside the lake, beneath the trees,
Fluttering and dancing in the breeze.

Continuous as the stars that shine
And twinkle on the Milky Way,
They stretched in never-ending line
Along the margin of a bay:
Ten thousand saw I at a glance,
Tossing their heads in sprightly dance.

=== **FILL IN THE BLANK** ===

11. **The figurative language used in the poem's first line is best described as** _____. (L.8.5)

12. **The figurative language used in the poem's last line is best described as** _____. (L.8.5)

4.1. VOCABULARY ACQUISITION AND USE

4. LANGUAGE

=== **MULTIPLE CHOICE** ===

13. What is the connotation of the underlined word? (L.8.5)

Tossing their heads in <u>sprightly</u> dance.

A. Negative   **B.** Positive   **C.** Neutral   **D.** Narrative

> ➤ *Directions: Read the passage and answer the questions below.*

Sometimes, she wondered if the pain would ever end. Day after day, she endured the excruciating agony in hopes that her body would heal. The doctor's report seemed promising, but the everlasting aches suggested otherwise. Although the surgery was successful, the recovery time felt like an eternity. Still, she remained hopeful that her body would soon begin to rebuild itself.

=== **MULTIPLE CHOICE** ===

14. What does the word *excruciating* mean? (L.8.4)

Day after day, she endured the <u>excruciating</u> agony in hopes that her body would heal.

A. Joyful   **B.** Irritated   **C.** Unexpected   **D.** Painful

15. Which definition best fits the context of the underlined word? (L.8.4)

The doctor's report seemed <u>promising</u>, but the everlasting aches suggested otherwise.

A. In the act of making a promise   **B.** Likely to fail
C. Likely to succeed   **D.** All of the above

16. What is the connotation of the underlined phrase? (L.8.5)

Although the surgery was successful, the recovery time <u>felt like an eternity</u>.

A. Positive   **B.** Negative   **C.** Neutral   **D.** None of the above

4. LANGUAGE

═══════════ **TRUE OR FALSE** ═══════════

17. **Figurative language is used to make literal comparisons in a text.** (L.8.5)

    A. True   **B.** False

18. **Connotation refers to a feeling or idea associated with a word.** (L.8.5)

    A. True   **B.** False

19. **Denotation is a type of figurative language.** (L.8.5)

    A. True   **B.** False

20. **Since the Greek prefix hyper- means "over" or "excessive," the word** *hyperactive* **refers to extreme activity.** (L.8.4)

    A. True   **B.** False

4.1. VOCABULARY ACQUISITION AND USE

4.2. CHAPTER REVIEW ➤➤➤

4. LANGUAGE

~~~~ 4.2. Chapter Review ~~~~

> ➢ *Directions: Read the passage and answer the questions below.*

CALL OF THE WILD

But the saloon-keeper let him alone, and in the morning four men entered and picked up the crate. More tormentors, Buck decided, for they were evil-looking creatures, ragged and unkempt; and he stormed and raged at them through the bars. They only laughed and poked sticks at him, which he promptly assailed with his teeth till he realized that that was what they wanted. Whereupon he lay down sullenly and allowed the crate to be lifted into a wagon. Then he, and the crate in which he was imprisoned, began a passage through many hands. Clerks in the express office took charge of him; he was carted about in another wagon; a truck carried him, with an assortment of boxes and parcels, upon a ferry steamer; he was trucked off the steamer into a great railway depot, and finally he was deposited in an express car.

=== **MULTIPLE CHOICE** ===

1. **What does the word *tormentors* mean?** (L.8.4)

   More <u>tormentors</u>, Buck decided, for they were evil-looking creatures, ragged and unkempt.

   A. Companions   **B.** Servants
   C. Tourists   **D.** Bullies

2. **Which phrase best helps to identify the meaning of *tormentors*?** (L.8.5)

   A. "they were evil-looking creatures"
   B. "the shed door rattled open"
   C. "he was deposited in an express car"
   D. "he realized that that was what they wanted"

4. LANGUAGE

3. **Which dictionary definition best fits the underlined word?** (L.8.4)

... he was trucked off the steamer into a great railway depot, and finally he was <u>deposited</u> in an express car.

A. Entrusted with someone for safekeeping

B. Left in a bank account

C. Placed or put down

D. Accumulated by a natural process

> ➤ *Directions: Read the passage and answer the questions below.*

A SEPARATE PEACE

I walked along Gilman Street, the best street in town. The houses were as handsome and as unusual as I remembered. Clever modernizations of old Colonial manses, extensions in Victorian wood, capacious Greek Revival temples lined the street, as impressive and just as forbidding as ever. I had rarely seen anyone go into one of them, or anyone playing on a lawn, or even an open window. Today with their failing ivy and stripped, moaning trees the houses looked both more elegant and more lifeless than ever.

Like all old, good schools, Devon did not stand isolated behind walls and gates but emerged naturally from the town which had produced it. So there was no sudden moment of encounter as I approached it; the houses along Gilman Street began to look more defensive, which meant that I was near the school, and then more exhausted, which meant that I was in it.

It was early afternoon and the grounds and buildings were deserted, since everyone was at sports. There was nothing to distract me as I made my way across a wide yard, called the Far Commons, and up to a building as red brick and balanced as the other major buildings, but with a large cupola and a bell and a clock and Latin over the doorway—the First Academy Building.

4.2. CHAPTER REVIEW

4. LANGUAGE

=== **MULTIPLE CHOICE** ===

4. **The Latin prefix de- means "away from." What does the word *deserted* mean in this sentence?** (L.8.4)

    The grounds and buildings were <u>deserted</u>, since everyone was at sports.

    A. Sweet   **B.** Empty   **C.** Dirty   **D.** Crowded

5. **Which phrase helps to identify the meaning of *deserted*?** (L.8.5)
    A. "I was near the school"
    B. "The houses were as handsome and as unusual as I remembered"
    C. "since everyone was at sports"
    D. "the houses looked both more elegant and more lifeless"

6. **The word *capacious* means "having lots of space inside." What is the connotation of this word as it is used in this text?** (L.8.5)

    The houses were as handsome and as unusual as I remembered. Clever modernizations of old Colonial manses, extensions in Victorian wood, <u>capacious</u> Greek Revival temples lined the street, as impressive and just as forbidding as ever.

    A. Positive   **B.** Negative   **C.** Neutral   **D.** Denotative

=== **FREE RESPONSE** ===

7. **Explain how you determined the connotation of the word *capacious* based on clues from the text.** (L.8.4, L.8.5)

    _____

    _____

    _____

    _____

4. LANGUAGE

_____

_____

_____

_____

_____

_____

_____

_____

_____

> ➤ *Directions: Read the passage and answer the questions below.*

LITTLE TUK

Yes, they called him Little Tuk, but it was not his real name; he had called himself so before he could speak plainly, and he meant it for Charles. It was all very well for those who knew him, but not for strangers.

Little Tuk was left at home to take care of his little sister, Gustava, who was much younger than himself. He had to learn his lessons at the same time, and the two things could not very well be performed together. The poor boy sat there with his sister on his lap, and sung to her all the songs he knew, and now and then he looked into his geography lesson that lay open before him. By the next morning he had to learn by heart all the towns in Zealand, and all that could be described of them.

His mother came home at last, and took little Gustava in her arms. Then Tuk ran to the window, and read so eagerly that he nearly read his eyes out; for it had become darker and darker every minute, and his mother had no money to buy a light.

prepaze

4. LANGUAGE

=== **MULTIPLE CHOICE** ===

8. **What does the phrase "at last" mean in the sentence below?** (L.8.5)

    His mother came home at last, and took little Gustava in her arms.
    A. She had finally come home after a long wait.
    B. She arrived after everyone else.
    C. She arrived at a very late hour at night.
    D. She was the only person remaining.

=== **TRUE OR FALSE** ===

9. **The poor boy sat there with his sister on his lap, and sung to her all the songs he knew. The use of the word "poor" refers to the family's socioeconomic status.** (L.8.4)

    A. True   **B.** False

10. **The phrase "learn his lessons at the same time" refers to Little Tuk acknowledging the mistakes he made in life.** (L.8.5)

    A. True   **B.** False

> ➤ *Directions: Read the passage and answer the questions below.*

LITTLE TUK

But now little Tuk was no longer in bed; all in a moment he found himself on horseback. Gallop, gallop, away he went, seated in front of a richly-attired knight, with a waving plume, who held him on the saddle, and so they rode through the wood by the old town of Wordingburg, which was very large and busy. The king's castle was surrounded by lofty towers, and radiant light streamed from all the windows. Within there were songs and dancing; King Waldemar and the young gaily-dressed ladies of the court were dancing together. Morning dawned, and as the sun rose, the whole city and the king's castle sank suddenly down together. One tower after another fell, till at last only one remained

...continued next page

4. LANGUAGE

standing on the hill where the castle had formerly been. The town now appeared small and poor. The school-boys read in their books, which they carried under their arms, that it contained two thousand inhabitants; but this was a mere boast, for it did not contain so many.

=== **MULTIPLE CHOICE** ===

11. **What is known about the knight since he is "richly-attired?"** (L.8.5)
    A. He has a lot of money in his pocket.
    B. He is dressed admirably.
    C. He is tired from the last battle he fought.
    D. He lived in that town for a long time.

12. **What does the word *inhabitants* mean?** (L.8.4)

    The town now appeared small and poor. The school-boys read in their books, which they carried under their arms, that it contained two thousand inhabitants.
    A. Animals that live in a specific region
    B. People who live in a certain place
    C. A habit or uncontrollable action
    D. Nove of the above

> ➤ *Directions: Read the passage and answer the questions below.*

CALL OF THE WILD

Buck lived at a big house in the sun-kissed Santa Clara Valley. Judge Miller's place, it was called. It stood back from the road, half hidden among the trees, through which glimpses could be caught of the wide cool veranda that ran around its four sides. The house was approached by graveled driveways which wound about through wide-spreading lawns and under the interlacing boughs of tall poplars. At the rear things were on even a more spacious scale than at the front. There were great stables, where a dozen grooms and boys held forth,

...continued next page

4.2. CHAPTER REVIEW

4. LANGUAGE

rows of vine-clad servants' cottages, an endless and orderly array of outhouses, long grape arbors, green pastures, orchards, and berry patches. Then there was the pumping plant for the artesian well, and the big cement tank where Judge Miller's boys took their morning plunge and kept cool in the hot afternoon.

MULTIPLE CHOICE

13. **What is the meaning of the word *sun-kissed?*** (L.8.4)

Buck lived at a big house in the <u>sun-kissed</u> Santa Clara Valley.

A. Loved by the sun
B. Hidden from the sun
C. Warmed by the sun
D. Powered by solar energy

14. **What is the meaning of the word *interlacing?*** (L.8.4)

The house was approached by graveled driveways which wound about through wide-spreading lawns and under the <u>interlacing</u> boughs of tall poplars.

A. Horrifying   **B.** Tangled   **C.** Shattered   **D.** Ancient

15. **What is the meaning of the word *array?*** (L.8.4)

There were great stables, where a dozen grooms and boys held forth, rows of vine-clad servants' cottages, an endless and orderly <u>array</u> of outhouses, long grape arbors, green pastures, orchards, and berry patches.

A. Arrangement
B. Occupation
C. Community
D. Agreement

4. LANGUAGE

16. Which dictionary definition best describes the word *plunge* as it is used in this sentence? (L.8.4)

Then there was the pumping plant for the artesian well, and the big cement tank where Judge Miller's boys took their morning <u>plunge</u> and kept cool in the hot afternoon.

A. To drop harshly
B. To fall into purposefully
C. An act of pushing unexpectedly
D. An act of jumping or diving quickly

> *Directions: Read the passage and answer the questions below.*

THE GIVER

Next, Mother, who held a prominent position at the Department of Justice, talked about her feelings. Today a repeat offender had been brought before her, someone who had broken the rules before. Someone who she hoped had been adequately and fairly punished, and who had been restored to his place: to his job, his home, his family unit. To see him brought before her a second time caused her overwhelming feelings of frustration and anger. And even guilt, that she hadn't made a difference in his life.

"I feel frightened, too, for him," she confessed. "You know that there's no third chance. The rules say that if there's a third transgression, he simply has to be released." Jonas shivered. He knew it happened. There was even a boy in his group of Elevens whose father had been released years before. No one ever mentioned it; the disgrace was unspeakable. It was hard to imagine.

=== MULTIPLE CHOICE ===

17. What is the meaning of the word *prominent*? (L.8.4)

Next, Mother, who held a <u>prominent</u> position at the Department of Justice, talked about her feelings.

A. Worthless   **B.** Well-known   **C.** Frightening   **D.** Disgraceful

4. LANGUAGE

18.   What is the meaning of the word *adequately?* (L.8.4)

Someone who she hoped had been <u>adequately</u> and fairly punished, and who had been restored to his place: to his job, his home, his family unit.

A. Jokingly   **B.** Properly   **C.** Mistakenly   **D.** Nearly

19.   What is the meaning of the word *transgression?* (RL.7.4)

The rules say that if there's a third <u>transgression</u>, he simply has to be released.

A. Protection   **B.** Motion

C. Violation   **D.** Misrepresentation

20.   What is the meaning of the word *disgrace?* (RL.7.4)

There was even a boy in his group of Elevens whose father had been released years before. No one ever mentioned it; the <u>disgrace</u> was unspeakable.

A. Grief   **B.** Shock   **C.** Glee   **D.** Shame

> *Directions: Read the passage and answer the questions below.*

TUCK EVERLASTING

For the second morning in a row, Winnie Foster woke early. Outside, in the ring of trees around the pond, the birds were celebrating, giving the new day a brass band's worth of greeting. Winnie freed herself from the twisted quilt and went to a window. Mist lay on the surface of the water, and the light was still pale. It looked unreal, and she felt, herself, unreal, waking where she had, with her hair wild and her dress all crumpled. She rubbed her eyes.

Through the dewy weeds below the window, a toad hopped suddenly into view and Winnie peered at it eagerly. But no—of course it wasn't the same toad. And remembering that other toad—her toad, she thought now, almost fondly—it seemed to her that she had been away from home for weeks. Then she heard a step on the loft stairs and thought, "Jesse!" At once her cheeks flamed.

4. LANGUAGE

═══════════════ **MULTIPLE CHOICE** ═══════════════

21. What does the underlined phrase most likely mean? (L.8.5)

Outside, in the ring of trees around the pond, the birds were celebrating, giving the new day <u>a brass band's worth of greeting.</u>

A. A brass band played in the parade nearby.
B. The birds' song was shiny like a brass band.
C. The birds sang loudly like a brass band playing instruments.
D. The birds' song was drowned out by a brass band playing loudly.

22. What does the underlined phrase most likely mean? (L.8.5)

<u>Mist lay on the surface of the water</u>, and the light was still pale.

A. A person named Mist is lying down in the water.
B. The mist was sleeping on top of the water.
C. The mist was quiet like a person lying down to sleep.
D. There were drops of mist on top of the water.

23. What is the meaning of the word *eagerly*? (L.8.4)

Through the dewy weeds below the window, a toad hopped suddenly into view and Winnie peered at it <u>eagerly</u>.

A. Excitedly   **B.** Doubtfully   **C.** Scarily   **D.** Gloomily

> ➤ *Directions: Read the passage and answer the questions below.*

FAHRENHEIT 451

He hung up his black-beetle-colored helmet and shined it, he hung his flameproof jacket neatly; he showered luxuriously, and then, whistling, hands in pockets, walked across the upper floor of the fire station and fell down the hole. At the last moment, when disaster seemed positive, he pulled his hands from his pockets and broke his fall by grasping the golden pole. He slid to a squeaking halt, the heels one inch from the concrete floor downstairs.

...continued next page

4.2. CHAPTER REVIEW

4. LANGUAGE

> He walked out of the fire station and along the midnight street toward the subway where the silent, air-propelled train slid soundlessly down its lubricated flue in the earth and let him out with a great puff of warm air onto the cream-tiled escalator rising to the suburb. Whistling, he let the escalator waft him into the still night air. He walked toward the comer, thinking little at all about nothing in particular. Before he reached the corner, however, he slowed as if a wind had sprung up from nowhere, as if someone had called his name.

=== **MULTIPLE CHOICE** ===

24. Which of the following best describes the literal meaning of the underlined phrase? (L.8.5)

At the last moment, when disaster seemed positive, he pulled his hands from his pockets and <u>broke his fall by grasping the golden pole</u>.

A. He cracked his fall into pieces on the pole.

B. He broke the pole as he fell down.

C. He broke his fall by turning a pole into gold.

D. He stopped himself from falling by grasping the pole.

25. Which of the following best describes the figurative language used in the above sentence? (L.8.5)

A. Idiom   **B.** Alliteration

C. Simile   **D.** Oxymoron

26. Which of the following best describes the literal meaning of the underlined phrase? (L.8.5)

Before he reached the corner, however, <u>he slowed as if a wind had sprung up from nowhere</u>, as if someone had called his name.

A. He slowed as if a wind had sprung up from nowhere.

B. The wind sprung up and blew him away.

C. The wind surprised him out of nowhere.

D. He slowed down suddenly.

       www.prepaze.com

4. LANGUAGE

27. Which of the following best describes the figurative language used in the above sentence?

    A. Hyperbole   **B.** Onomatopoeia

    C. Simile   **D.** Personification

> ➤ *Directions: Read the passage and answer the questions below.*

THE GREAT GATSBY

The rain cooled about half-past three to a damp mist, through which occasional thin drops swam like dew. Gatsby looked with vacant eyes through a copy of *Clay's Economics*, starting at the Finnish tread that shook the kitchen floor, and peering toward the bleared windows from time to time as if a series of invisible but alarming happenings were taking place outside. Finally he got up and informed me, in an uncertain voice, that he was going home.

=== **MULTIPLE CHOICE** ===

28. What does the underlined phrase most likely mean? (L.8.5)

The rain cooled about half-past three to a damp mist, through which <u>occasional thin drops swam like dew</u>.

    A. A fierce rainstorm developed.

    B. A few small raindrops continued to fall.

    C. The raindrops grew arms and began to swim.

    D. The raindrops magically transformed into dew.

29. What does the underlined phrase most likely mean? (L.8.5)

<u>Gatsby looked with vacant eyes</u> through a copy of *Clay's Economics*, starting at the Finnish tread that shook the kitchen floor ...

    A. Gatsby is inside of a vacant, empty apartment.

    B. Gatsby is thinking about going on vacation.

    C. Gatsby is blind and his eye sockets are empty.

    D. Gatsby is staring blankly with little expression.

4.2. CHAPTER REVIEW

30. What does the word bleared mean? (L.8.5)

...and peering toward the <u>bleared</u> windows from time to time...

A. Dimmed or blurred   **B.** Cracked and broken

C. Made of glass   **D.** Widely opened

4.2. CHAPTER REVIEW

 www.prepaze.com

END OF YEAR ASSESSMENT

END OF YEAR ASSESMENT

> *Directions: Read the passage and answer the questions below.*

BOOKER T. AND W.E.B.

"It seems to me," said Booker T.,
"That all you folks have missed the boat
Who shout about the right to vote,
And spend vain days and sleepless nights
In uproar over civil rights.
Just keep your mouths shut, do not grouse,
But work, and save, and buy a house."

"I don't agree," said W.E.B.
"For what can property avail
If dignity and justice fail?
Unless you help to make the laws,
They'll steal your house with trumped-up clause.
A rope's as tight, a fire as hot,
No matter how much cash you've got.
Speak soft, and try your little plan,
But as for me, I'll be a man."

"It seems to me," said Booker T.—
"I don't agree,"
Said W.E.B.

END OF YEAR ASSESSMENT

===== **TRUE OR FALSE** =====

1. **The interaction between the subjects of the poem creates a sense of humor.** (RL.8.6)

   A. True   **B.** False

2. **Booker T.'s perspective is less assertive than W.E.B's point of view.** (RL.8.6)

   A. True   **B.** False

3. **Which statement best describes the conflicting views in this poem?** (RL.7.6)

   A. The poem is an argument between two points of view on civil rights.

   B. The poem is a debate about who was a better civil rights leader.

   C. The poem is a ballad about two different events that occurred during the Civil Rights Movement.

   D. The poem does not present any conflicting views.

> *Directions: Read the passages and answer the questions below.*

FRANKENSTEIN

As he said this, Frankenstein led the way across the ice: I followed. My heart was full, and I did not answer him; but, as I proceeded, I weighed the various arguments that he had used, and determined at least to listen to his tale. I was partly urged by curiosity, and compassion confirmed my resolution. I had hitherto supposed him to be guilty, and I eagerly sought a confirmation or denial of this opinion. For the first time, also, I felt what the duties of a creator towards his creature were, and that I ought to render him happy before I complained of his wickedness. These motives urged me to comply with his demand. We crossed the ice, therefore, and ascended the opposite rock. The air was cold, and the rain again began to descend: we entered the hut, the fiend with an air of exultation, I with a heavy heart and depressed spirits. But I consented to listen; and, seating myself by the fire which my odious companion had lighted, he thus began his tale.

 prepaze

END OF YEAR ASSESSMENT

=== **MULTIPLE CHOICE** ===

4. **What is the central theme of the passage?** (RL.8.2)

   A. The scientist realizes that he is responsible for Frankenstein's creation and actions.

   B. The scientist realizes that the monster is the only person responsible for his actions.

   C. The scientist realizes that an inventor is not responsible for the actions of what he created.

   D. None of the above

5. **Which of these lines best demonstrate the central theme?** (RL.8.2, RL.8.3)

   A. There can be no community between you and me; we are enemies. Begone, or let us try our strength in a fight, in which one must fall.

   B. For the first time, also, I felt what the duties of a creator towards his creature were, and that I ought to render him happy before I complained of his wickedness.

   C. ... the caves of ice, which I only do not fear, are a dwelling to me, and the only one which man does not grudge.

   D. The air was cold, and the rain again began to descend

> ➤ *Directions: Read the passage and answer the questions below.*

THE JUNGLE BOOK

It was the jackal—Tabaqui, the Dish-licker—and the wolves of India despise Tabaqui because he runs about making mischief, and telling tales, and eating rags and pieces of leather from the village rubbish-heaps. But they are afraid of him too, because Tabaqui, more than anyone else in the jungle, is apt to go mad, and then he forgets that he was ever afraid of anyone, and runs through the forest biting everything in his way. Even the tiger runs and hides when little Tabaqui goes mad, for madness is the most disgraceful thing that can overtake a wild creature. We call it hydrophobia, but they call it dewanee—the madness—and run.

...continued next page

END OF YEAR ASSESSMENT

"Enter, then, and look," said Father Wolf stiffly, "but there is no food here."

"For a wolf, no," said Tabaqui, "but for so mean a person as myself a dry bone is a good feast. Who are we, the Gidur-log [the jackal people], to pick and choose?" He scuttled to the back of the cave, where he found the bone of a buck with some meat on it, and sat cracking the end merrily.

"All thanks for this good meal," he said, licking his lips. "How beautiful are the noble children! How large are their eyes! And so young too! Indeed, indeed, I might have remembered that the children of kings are men from the beginning."

Now, Tabaqui knew as well as anyone else that there is nothing so unlucky as to compliment children to their faces. It pleased him to see Mother and Father Wolf look uncomfortable.

Tabaqui sat still, rejoicing in the mischief that he had made, and then he said spitefully:

"Shere Khan, the Big One, has shifted his hunting grounds. He will hunt among these hills for the next moon, so he has told me."

Shere Khan was the tiger who lived near the Waingunga River, twenty miles away.

"He has no right!" Father Wolf began angrily—"By the Law of the Jungle he has no right to change his quarters without due warning. He will frighten every head of game within ten miles, and I—I have to kill for two, these days."

===== MULTIPLE CHOICE =====

6. **How does the information that Shere Khan is hunting affect Father Wolfe?** (RL.8.1)

   A. It excites him because Shere Khan is protecting them from hunters.

   B. It makes him jealous that Shere Khan is a superior hunter.

   C. It frightens him because he is scared of what will happen to Shere Khan.

   D. It angers him that Shere Khan is breaking the rules of the jungle.

END OF YEAR ASSESSMENT

7. **Which one of the following lines demonstrates how Tabaqui is trying to cause trouble with Father and Mother Wolf?** (RL.8.1, RL.8.3)

  A. "For a wolf, no," said, "but for so mean a person as myself a dry bone is a good feast."

  B. "All thanks for this good meal," he said, licking his lips. "How beautiful are the noble children!"

  C. It pleased him to see Mother and Father Wolf look uncomfortable.

  D. All of the above

> ➤ *Directions: Read the passages and answer the questions below.*

GENESIS 25:27-34 NIV

FROM GENESIS, A BOOK IN THE BIBLE

The boys grew up, and Esau became a skillful hunter, a man of the open country, while Jacob was content to stay at home among the tents.

Isaac, who had a taste for wild game, loved Esau, but Rebekah loved Jacob.

Once when Jacob was cooking some stew, Esau came in from the open country, famished. 30 He said to Jacob, "Quick, let me have some of that red stew! I'm famished!" (That is why he was also called Edom.)

Jacob replied, "First sell me your birthright."

"Look, I am about to die," Esau said. "What good is the birthright to me?"

But Jacob said, "Swear to me first." So he swore an oath to him, selling his birthright to Jacob.

Then Jacob gave Esau some bread and some lentil stew. He ate and drank, and then got up and left.

So Esau despised his birthright.

END OF YEAR ASSESSMENT

END OF YEAR ASSESSMENT

TWO BROTHERS

The elder of the boys looked roguish and enterprising. He took a delight in reading of the forces of nature, of the sun and the moon; no fairy tale pleased him so much. Oh, how beautiful it must be, he thought, to go on voyages of discovery, or to find out how to imitate the wings of birds and then to be able to fly! Yes, to find that out was the right thing. Father was right, and mother was right- truth holds the world together.

The younger brother was quieter, and buried himself entirely in his books. When he read about Jacob dressing himself in sheep-skins to personify Esau, and so to usurp his brother's birthright, he would clench his little fist in anger against the deceiver; when he read of tyrants and of the injustice and wickedness of the world, tears would come into his eyes, and he was quite filled with the thought of the justice and truth which must and would triumph.

MULTIPLE CHOICE

---

8. **How does the second passage refer to elements from the first passage?** (RL.8.9)
   A. The second text includes a flashback to events from the first text.
   B. The second text takes place in the same setting as the first, during a different time era.
   C. The second text refers to characters from the first text.
   D. Both texts include the same characters and plot.

9. **How is the structure similar in both texts?** (RL.8.5)
   A. Both texts are written in an expository style.
   B. Both texts are written in a narrative style.
   C. Both texts are written in a persuasive style.
   D. There are no similarities in the structure and style of these texts.

prepaze

END OF YEAR ASSESSMENT

> ➤ *Directions: Read the passage and answer the questions below.*

People use many different modes of transportation. However, certain types of transportation are not useful for international travel. For example, it is not possible for travelers to walk or drive across the ocean. Although boating is a feasible option, flying is the quickest route. A boat trip could take several days, while a plane ride would only last a few hours. Also, some people do not like to travel by water due to seasickness. This is another advantage of taking a flight instead. When planning to travel overseas, it is best to take an airplane.

═══ MULTIPLE CHOICE ═══

END OF YEAR ASSESSMENT

10. What is the central idea of this passage? (RI.8.2)
   A. People cannot walk or drive across the ocean.
   B. People use many different modes of transportation.
   C. When planning to travel overseas, it is best to take an airplane.
   D. Traveling is my favorite hobby.

11. Which sentence best supports the central idea of this passage? (RI.8.2)
   A. They could travel by boat, but flying is the quickest route.
   B. People use many different modes of transportation.
   C. Boats can travel to many different countries.
   D. When planning to travel overseas, it is best to take an airplane.

12. Which sentence does NOT support the central idea of this passage? (RI.8.2)
   A. They could travel by boat, but flying is the quickest route.
   B. When planning to travel overseas, it is best to take an airplane.
   C. Airplanes are bad for the environment.
   D. A boat trip could take several days, while a plane ride would only last a few hours.

END OF YEAR ASSESSMENT

13. **Which sentence could also summarize the central idea of this passage?** (RI.8.2)

A. Flying is the quickest and most cost-efficient way to travel overseas.

B. Many people prefer to walk instead of driving

C. Boats can cause seasickness.

D. People should be careful when traveling overseas.

> *Directions: Read the passage and answer the questions below.*

THE WHITE HOUSE COOKBOOK

Pour all in well-buttered cake-pans. While the cake is baking care should be taken that no cold air enters the oven, only when necessary to see that the cake is baking properly; the oven should be an even, moderate heat, not too cold or too hot; much depends on this for success. Cake is often spoiled by being looked at too often when first put into the oven. The heat should be tested before the cake is put in, which can be done by throwing on the floor of the oven a tablespoonful of new flour. If the flour takes fire, or assumes a dark brown color, the temperature is too high and the oven must be allowed to cool; if the flour remains white after the lapse of a few seconds, the temperature is too low. When the oven is of the proper temperature the flour will slightly brown and look slightly scorched.

Another good way to test the heat, is to drop a few spoonfuls of the cake batter on a small piece of buttered letter paper, and place it in the oven during the finishing of the cake, so that the piece will be baked before putting in the whole cake; if the little drop of cake batter bakes evenly without burning around the edge, it will be safe to put the whole cake in the oven. Then, again, if the oven seems too hot, fold a thick brown paper double, and lay on the bottom of the oven; then after the cake has risen, put a thick brown paper over the top, or butter well a thick white paper and lay carefully over the top.

END OF YEAR ASSESSMENT

END OF YEAR ASSESSMENT

═══ **TRUE OR FALSE** ═══

14. The author's purpose is to inform the reader about proper baking techniques. (RI.8.6)

    A. True   **B.** False

15. Cake is often spoiled by being looked at too often when first put into the oven. The term "spoiled" refers to childish behavior in this sentence. (RI.8.4)

    A. True   **B.** False

═══ **MULTIPLE CHOICE** ═══

16. How is the text structured in order to develop key concepts? (RI.8.5)

    A. In chronological order
    B. In a cause/effect format
    C. In a problem/solution format
    D. In a descriptive style

> ➤ *Directions: Read the passage and answer the questions below.*

COUNTRIES OF THE WORLD: NORWAY

Norway is the most western, northern, and eastern of the three Scandinavian countries and has borders with Sweden, Finland, and Russia. Norway is well known for its amazing and varied scenery. The fjords in the west of the country are long narrow inlets, flanked on either side by tall mountains where the sea penetrates far inland. By far, the major part of the land is a rocky wilderness, and, therefore, Norway has large, completely unpopulated areas, many of which have been converted to national parks. Even outside the national parks, much of the land is unspoiled nature. With a population of only 5 million people, Norway is one of Europe's most sparsely populated countries. Almost half the length of Norway is north of the Arctic Circle, and because it so far north, the sun does not rise above the horizon in the winter months. You can often see the northern lights, or aurora borealis, in Norway during the darker months.

END OF YEAR ASSESSMENT

===== **MULTIPLE CHOICE** =====

17. **Why is Norway's scenery famous?** (RI.8.1)
   A. The scenery is famous because it borders Russia, Sweden, and Finland.
   B. The scenery is famous because it is located in northern Europe.
   C. The scenery is famous because of its variety.
   D. The scenery is famous because of its parks.

18. **What is most likely the reason people can see the aurora borealis?** (RI.8.1, RI.8.3)
   A. The sun rises high above the horizon in winter.
   B. Norway is a country in the far North part of the world
   C. The mountains make the aurora borealis easy to see.
   D. The parks have open areas, which give great views of the sky.

> ➤ *Directions: Read the passage and answer the questions below.*

COUNTRIES OF THE WORLD: Sweden

Sweden is the largest of the Nordic countries, with a population of about 10 million. It borders Norway and Finland and is connected to Denmark via the bridge of Öresund. Since 1815, Sweden and Switzerland are the only two European countries that have not been involved in a war. The standard of living and life expectancy of Swedish citizens ranks among the highest in the world. Sweden is less populated than most other parts of Europe. Its cities are located along the coast and rivers, but it is the great outdoors that is the main attraction, with many national parks and nature reserves. Due to the law of Allemansrätten (Everyman's Right), most of Sweden's nature can be freely accessed unless the area is specifically protected. This means that you can walk, camp, and swim almost everywhere in Sweden.

END OF YEAR ASSESSMENT

=== **MULTIPLE CHOICE** ===

19. **What is the central idea of this text?** (RI.8.2)

   A. This text is mainly about Sweden.

   B. This text is mainly about Norway and Sweden.

   C. This text is mainly about people in Sweden.

   D. This text is mainly about camping in Sweden.

20. **Which of these sentences best relates to the previous text?** (RI.8.9)

   A. "This means that you can walk, camp, and swim almost everywhere in Sweden."

   B. "It borders Norway and Finland and is connected to Denmark via the bridge of Öresund."

   C. "Sweden is less populated than most other parts of Europe."

   D. "Since 1815, Sweden and Switzerland are the only two European countries that have not been involved in a war."

21. **What is most likely the reason why Sweden has a small population?** (RI.8.1, RI.8.3)

   A. The outdoors and national parks are more important than the big cities.

   B. Sweden will not allow the cities to become overpopulated.

   C. The wars it has been involved in caused the population to decrease.

   D. Sweden has a very high standard of living, which would decrease if there were more people.

22. **According to the text, what types of areas are protected from people visiting?** (RI.8.1, RI.8.3)

   A. big cities

   B. national parks

   C. mountains

   D. The article does not give a reason.

END OF YEAR ASSESSMENT

> *Directions: Read the passage and answer the questions below.*

BOTTLED WATER Is Harmful

Whenever you buy and drink water from a bottle, believe it or not, you are paying more for the plastic bottle than you are for the water. What's worse is that you are contributing to a Mount Everest of waste that will be in existence for your great, great, great 17-more-times-great grandchildren to see. It takes 450 years for a plastic water bottle to disintegrate. Every year people throw between 22 and 35 billion of them away. Many end up in the ocean, but more are left to go into landfills. It also takes a huge amount of energy to make these environmental destroyers: It takes 1/4 of a bottle of oil to produce a single water bottle.

Bottled water doesn't mean it's pure, or comes from a sustainable source, either. Some bottled water comes from underground water reserves, which can make droughts more severe.

=== **MULTIPLE CHOICE** ===

23. **Which sentence best describes the author's main claim in this text?**
    (RI.8.8)
    A. "Bottled water doesn't mean it's pure, or comes from a sustainable source, either."
    B. "It takes 1/4 of a bottle of oil to produce a single water bottle."
    C. "It takes 450 years for a plastic water bottle to disintegrate."
    D. "What's worse is that you are contributing to a Mount Everest of waste..."

24. **How does the author support his or her claim in the text?** (RI.8.8)
    A. The author gives quotations from experts to support the claim.
    B. The author cites statistical data to support the claim.
    C. The author cites a research study to support the claim.
    D. The author quotes a reputable source to support the claim.

END OF YEAR ASSESSMENT

25. Which of the following would be considered the best example of relevant evidence for this topic? (RI.8.8)

   A. An interview with someone who buys bottled water.

   B. A quote from a newspaper article about the bottled water industry.

   C. The results of a research study about the environmental effects of bottled water.

   D. A logical explanation of why people should not drink bottled water.

> ➤ *Directions: Read the passage and answer the questions below.*

THE LIFE OF CHRISTOPHER COLUMBUS

Columbus's father-in-law had himself been the Portuguese governor of the island of Porto Santo, where he had founded a colony. He, therefore, was interested in western explorations, and probably from him Columbus collected some of the statements which are known to have influenced him, with regard to floating matters from the West, which are constantly borne upon that island by the great currents of the sea.

It is easy now to see and to say that Columbus himself was singularly well fitted to take the charge of the expedition of discovery. He was an excellent sailor and at the same time he was a learned geographer and a good mathematician. He was living in Portugal, the kings of which country had, for many years, fostered the exploration of the coast of Africa, and were pushing expeditions farther and farther South.

AMERICAN LEADERS AND HEROES

While at Lisbon, Columbus married a woman far above him in social position, and went with her to live on a little island of the Madeiras, where her family had business interests. Meanwhile he was turning over in his mind schemes for a future voyage to the countries of the Far East. His native city, Genoa, had grown rich in trading in the silks, spices, and precious stones of the Indies, but the journey overland was dangerous, and a water route was much desired.

...continued next page

END OF YEAR ASSESSMENT

This need the Portuguese had felt along with the rest of Europe, and for a long time Portuguese sea-captains had been slowly but surely finding their way down the west coast of Africa, in search of a passage around the southern cape. This route would be easier and cheaper than the old one through the Mediterranean and across Asia. But Columbus thought out a more daring course, by which he planned to sail directly west from the Canary Islands, across the Atlantic Ocean, expecting at the end of his voyage to find the far-famed Indies.

MULTIPLE CHOICE

26. What is emphasized in the first source regarding Columbus's family compared to the second source? (RI.8.9)

A. Support from his father-in-law **B.** Voyages taken with his wife

C. Life with his parents **D.** Opposition from his siblings

FREE RESPONSE

27. How is the portrayal of Columbus different in these texts? (RI.8.9)

_____

_____

_____

_____

_____

_____

_____

_____

   prepaze

END OF YEAR ASSESSMENT

_____

_____

_____

_____

_____

_____

_____

_____

_____

_____

END OF YEAR ASSESSMENT

> ➤ _Directions: Read the questions and select the best answer choice._

===== **MULTIPLE CHOICE** =====

28. Which medium would be the best to use when presenting information about ancient artwork? (RI.8.7)

   A. Print   **B.** Audio

   C. Photos   **D.** None of the above

29. Which of the following statements is NOT true? (RI.8.9)

   A. A school library does contain both reliable and inaccurate information.

   B. Some resources may state facts contrary to what you have previously learned about a topic.

   C. Print books are not as reliable as digital tools.

   D. All of these statements are true.

END OF YEAR ASSESSMENT

30. **A student claims that all dogs should be required to receive flea preventative medicine. Which of the following is a counterclaim for this topic?** (RI.8.8, W.8.1)

    A. Some people assert that dogs do not need to be on a flea preventative medicine.

    B. Data show a huge difference in the number of vet trips for those dogs who are not on a flea preventative medicine, compared to those who are.

    C. A recent survey shows that most dog owners are in favor of preventive medicine.

    D. All of these statements are counterclaims to this argument.

31. **Which example or examples would best support an article discussing solar energy?** (W.8.2)

    A. Solar energy is defined as gaining the light and energy from the sun in order to use it in the home.

    B. Companies in our area that provide solar energy include Energy Solutions, Inc. and Solar Speed.

    C. Electricity can be replaced with solar energy.

    D. All of the above

32. **Which of the following is a purpose for the introduction of a story?** (W.8.3)

    A. To provide a sense of closure

    B. To introduce the characters

    C. To present the conflict

    D. To explain the story's genre

33. **A student writes about the likelihood of farmers becoming obsolete in the near future. However, the teacher assigned the students to write about a popular modern career. What is the student's error?** (W.8.4)

    A. The task   **B.** The purpose

    C. The audience   **D.** The style

prepaze

34. Why is it important to rewrite your essay as a final draft? (W.8.5)

  A. Because people should not make mistakes when writing.

  B. Because the teacher asks you to do so.

  C. Because this is the first step in the writing process.

  D. Because this final step in the writing process eliminates errors.

TRUE OR FALSE

35. A printed encyclopedia is not a credible source if it was written a long time ago. (W.8.1)

  A. True   **B.** False

36. Transition words such as "furthermore" and "in addition to" can help to develop your essay topic. (W.8.2)

  A. True   **B.** False

37. Since Carol is completing a narrative writing assignment, she does not need to follow the process of planning, revising, editing, and rewriting. (W.8.5)

  A. True   **B.** False

38. All writing pieces have an intended audience. (W.8.4)

  A. True   **B.** False

WRITING PROMPT

39. Write a personal narrative essay about a memorable experience that changed one of your primary characteristics. (W.8.3)

_____

_____

_____

END OF YEAR ASSESSMENT

_____

_____

_____

_____

_____

_____

_____

_____

_____

_____

_____

_____

_____

_____

_____

_____

_____

_____

END OF YEAR ASSESSMENT

NAME: .... **DATE:** ....

END OF YEAR ASSESSMENT

_____

_____

_____

_____

_____

_____

_____

_____

_____

_____

_____

_____

_____

_____

_____

_____

_____

END OF YEAR ASSESSMENT

> ➤ *Directions: Read the passage and answer the questions below.*

ROLL OF THUNDER, HEAR MY CRY

Sitting so close to the desk, I could see that the covers of the books, a motley red, were badly worn and that the gray edges of the pages had been marred by pencils, crayons, and ink. My anticipation at having my own book ebbed to a sinking disappointment. But Miss Crocker continued to beam as she called each fourth grader to her desk and, recording a number in her roll book, handed him or her a book. As I returned from my trip to her desk, I noticed the first graders anxiously watching the disappearing pile.

Miss Crocker must have noticed them too, for as I sat down she said, "Don't worry, little ones, there are plenty of readers for you too. See there on Miss Davis's desk." Wide eyes turned to the covered teacher's platform directly in front of them and an audible sigh of relief swelled in the room.

=== **MULTIPLE CHOICE** ===

40. What is the meaning of the word *marred?* (L.8.4)

... the gray edges of the pages had been <u>marred</u> by pencils, crayons, and ink.

A. Received   **B.** Blemished   **C.** Pointed   **D.** Cracked

41. What is most likely the meaning of the underlined phrase? (L.8.5)

My anticipation at having my own book <u>ebbed to a sinking disappointment</u>.

A. The narrator sank to the floor disappointedly.
B. The narrator tossed the book into a pool of water.
C. The narrator lost her excitement about having a book.
D. The narrator's book was disappointingly heavy.

END OF YEAR ASSESSMENT

42. The Latin prefix audi- means "to hear". What is the meaning of the word *audible*? (L.8.4)

Wide eyes turned to the covered teacher's platform directly in front of them and an <u>audible</u> sigh of relief swelled in the room.

A. Easily heard
C. Unheard

B. Faint and muffled
D. Painful to the ears

> *Directions: Read the passage and answer the questions below.*

ROLL OF THUNDER, HEAR MY CRY

By the end of October the rain had come, falling heavily upon the six-inch layer of dust which had had its own way for more than two months. At first the rain had merely splotched the dust, which seemed to be rejoicing in its own resiliency and laughing at the heavy drops thudding against it; but eventually the dust was forced to surrender to the mastery of the rain and it churned into a fine red mud that oozed between our toes and slopped against our ankles as we marched miserably to and from school. To shield us from the rain, Mama issued us dried calfskins which we flung over our heads and shoulders like stiff cloaks.

We were not very fond of the skins, for once they were wet they emitted a musty odor which seeped into our clothing and clung to our skins. We preferred to do without them; unfortunately, Mama cared very little about what we preferred.

=== MULTIPLE CHOICE ===

43. What is the meaning of the word *resiliency*? (L.8.4)

... which seemed to be rejoicing in its own <u>resiliency</u> and laughing at the heavy drops thudding against it.

A. Dampness
C. Strength

B. Humor
D. Fragility

END OF YEAR ASSESSMENT

44. What is most likely the meaning of the underlined phrase? (L.8.5)

... but eventually <u>the dust was forced to surrender to the mastery of the rain</u> and it churned into a fine red mud that oozed between our toes ...

A. The dust had to accept that the rain was more skilled.
B. The dust became overpowered by the rain.
C. The dust began to dissolve in the rain.
D. The rain could not dampen the dust.

45. What is the meaning of the word *emitted*? (L.8.4)

We were not very fond of the skins, for once they were wet they <u>emitted</u> a musty odor which seeped into our clothing and clung to our skins.

A. Scented   **B.** Released   **C.** Retracted   **D.** Expected

ANSWER KEY

8. Answer: A

Explanation: The sentence, "Chef Misty kneaded the dough strenuously, with all of her might" best illustrates the character's actions.

9. Answer: D

Explanation: A story's conclusion reflects on past events from the story.

10. Answer: B

Explanation: This statement is false. An interview with a famous skateboarder would be a credible source of evidence to develop this topic.

11. Answer: B

Explanation: This statement is false. Mary could also include her personal viewpoint and logical reasoning on the topic.

12. Answer: A

Explanation: This statement is true. Writers should include definitions of key terms in an informative essay.

13. Answer: A

Explanation: This statement is true. If a student writes the exact words from a source without giving credit to the author, he or she would be committing plagiarism.

14. Answer: A

Explanation: This statement is true. A flashback is a narrative technique that introduces events that happened before the beginning of the story.

15. Answer: B

Explanation: This statement is false. Technical vocabulary is not an effective technique in narrative development.

16. Answer: Answers will vary

Explanation: Students should be able to explain how the credibility of the resources used can affect the outcome of an essay.

17. Answer: Answers will vary

Explanation: Students should be able to explain how domain-specific vocabulary is used to develop a topic. Karen could use key terms and definitions that are relevant to the topic.

18. Answer: Answers will vary

Explanation: Students should be able to explain how pacing affects narrative writing. Sarah's story may seem rushed and may lack key events if not properly paced.

19. Answer: Answers will vary

Explanation: Students should be able to write a paragraph that clearly states the claim and introduces ideas.

20. Answer: Answers will vary

Explanation: Students should be able to write a conclusion that follows from and reflects on the narrated events.

3.2. Production and Distribution

1. Answer: D

Explanation: The teacher should first explain the task so the students understand the general nature of the assignment.

2. Answer: C

Explanation: The essay would not clearly convey Karen's ideas.

3. Answer: B

Explanation: The purpose of this task would be to inform the reader about how these events are connected.

4. Answer: C

Explanation: A classmate with an unbiased view on the topic would be the best person to objectively peer edit her writing.

3. WRITING

prepaze

ANSWER KEY

5. Answer: A

Explanation: It is best to replace certain words with synonyms in order to avoid repetition. It is not necessary to completely rewrite the text.

6. Answer: B

Explanation: Carol has written a story that is not within the genre and historical context that the teacher assigned so it did not match the purpose and task.

7. Answer: inform

Explanation: The main purpose for writing about the life cycles of frogs and toads would be to inform the audience.

8. Answer: task

Explanation: Robin's teacher asks the class to write about their favorite time to study. Robin writes about her favorite subject to study. She did not address the appropriate task.

9. Answer: conclusion

Explanation: As Sarah organizes her informative essay about British soldiers, she will include an introduction, body paragraphs, and a conclusion.

10. Answer: outline

Explanation: Pete is writing an essay. He could use an outline to help structure his ideas before he begins writing.

11. Answer: audience

Explanation: Jake is writing an article about toys that should be recalled due to child injuries. This article's intended audience is parents and teachers.

12. Answer: transition

Explanation: In Sarah's narrative writing, she uses transitional words/phrases to show the relationships among experiences and events.

13. Answer: B

Explanation: This statement is false. It is important to consider the audience before you begin the writing process.

14. Answer: A

Explanation: This statement is true. The student wrote her assignment in the wrong style.

15. Answer: B

Explanation: This statement is false. Kevin should check for grammatical or spelling errors during the editing process. The revision process is for rewriting, adding and/ or omitting text.

16. Answer: A

Explanation: This statement is true. It is best to research the topic before writing.

17. Answer: Answers will vary

Explanation: Students should be able to identify the appropriate purpose and style of a writing task. An essay that explains how the candy is made could be written in an expository style to inform the audience.

18. Answer: Answers will vary

Explanation: Students should be able to explain how writing style is related to the writer's purpose. Ex.: Expository writing is used when the writer's purpose is to inform and explain.

19. Answer: Answers will vary

Explanation: Students should be able to identify strategies for revising unclear writing. Ex.: Tiffany can rewrite her essay, starting with more research to find support for her claim.

20. Answer: Answers will vary

Explanation: Students should be able to identify strategies for revising poorly deve-loped writing. A good conclusion should follows from and supports the information or presented. Ex.: George can strengthen his conclusion by summarizing information from the entire essay, not just the introduction.

ANSWER KEY

3.3. Chapter Review

1. Answer: A
Explanation: It provides the format for writing her essay in a persuasive way. Cara will most likely write her essay in a persuasive writing style.

2. Answer: D
Explanation: Results from a survey conducted about popular game shows would best support this topic.

3. Answer: C
Explanation: This is an example of a narrative dialogue.

4. Answer: A
Explanation: The quoted material will provide a firsthand account of the support given during a crisis.

5. Answer: D
Explanation: It is best to start over so that your writing completely pertains to the prompt.

6. Answer: A
Explanation: It is best to write about a topic that you are familiar with in order to apply previous knowledge.

7. Answer: B
Explanation: In persuasive writing, it is best to take a clear stance on the issue and support it.

8. Answer: B
Explanation: The word also would best link these two sentences together.

9. Answer: C
Explanation: Mary should first introduce the characters through descriptions and events.

10. Answer: C
Explanation: Statistics from a health organization about job-related injuries would best support this topic.

11. Answer: credible or reliable
Explanation: An unverified website about the Civil War may not be a credible source of evidence.

12. Answer: expository or explanatory
Explanation: This is an example of expository writing.

13. Answer: characters
Explanation: A good narrative should reveal the thoughts, feelings, and actions of the characters throughout the text.

14. Answer: narrative
Explanation: A diary entry is an example of personal narrative writing.

15. Answer: purpose
Explanation: A writing prompt describes the task and purpose of an assignment.

16. Answer: Answers will vary
Explanation: Students should be able to explain how specific details can be used to support a claim. This statement could be used to connect the evidence to the claim. Ex.: There are about 575 calories in the average lunch. I believe that this is a sufficient number of calories and should not be reduced.

17. Answer: Answers will vary
Explanation: Students should be able to explain how domain-specific vocabulary can be used to develop a topic.

18. Answer: Answers will vary
Explanation: Students should be able to explain how transition words convey sequence in a story.

3. WRITING

prepaze

ANSWER KEY

19.   Answer: Answers will vary

Explanation: Students should be able to explain how a writing task can be developed in different styles and structures. Ex.: A text about an influential person could be written in a narrative or expository style.

20. Answer: Answers will vary

Explanation: Students should demonstrate an understanding of the complete writing process. After revisions and edits are complete, the final draft will serve as the highest quality version.

21.   Answer: A

Explanation: This statement is true. In argumentative writing, the writer should state his/her opinion directly.

22.   Answer: B

Explanation: This statement is false. An informative essay about restaurants should not include the writer's opinion and personal experience.

23.   Answer: B

Explanation: This statement is false. Narrative writing can be used to develop real or imaginary experiences.

24.   Answer: A

Explanation: This statement is true. A persuasive essay about traffic safety could include statistics about the number of recent car crashes.

25.   Answer: A

Explanation: This statement is true. During the writing process, it is important to plan and organize your ideas before you begin writing.

26.   Answer: Answers will vary

Explanation: Students should be able to write a paragraph that clearly introduces and supports their claims.

27.   Answer: Answers will vary

Explanation: Students should be able to rewrite the text using transition words to connect ideas. Ex.: The key to proper oral care is to follow a daily regimen. First, carefully floss your teeth to remove any food residue.

28.   Answer: Answers will vary

Explanation: Students should be able to write a dialogue that reveals the thoughts, feelings, and actions of the characters.

29.   Answer: Answers will vary

Explanation: Students should be able to write a counterclaim that opposes the original claim with clear reasons and relevant evidence.

30.   Answer: Answers will vary

Explanation: Students should be able to write an informative essay that is well developed and organized, using proper technique.

4. LANGUAGE

4.1. Vocabulary Acquisition and Use

1.   Answer: B

Explanation: The word *gleamed* means shone in the context of the text.

2.   Answer: C

Explanation: "The light from the corridor" helps to identify the meaning of the word *beamed*.

3.   Answer: D

Explanation: The word *fretted* means worried in the context of the text.

4.   Answer: A

Explanation: "Paced the floor" helps to identify the meaning of the word *fretted*.

5. Answer: B
Explanation: The word *revision* means corrections in the context of the text.

6. Answer: C
Explanation: The word *raucous* means disturbingly harsh and loud in the context of this text.

7. Answer: D
Explanation: The phrase "The house jumped up in a gorging fire" means that the house burst into flames.

8. Answer: A
Explanation: Personification gives human qualities to something that is non-human. This phrase gives human qualities to a house.

9. Answer: C
Explanation: The phrase "The flapping pigeon-winged books died on the porch" that the book pages flapped like wings in the fire.

10. Answer: B
Explanation: A metaphor is a figure of speech that is used to compare things that are actually different. This phrase compares pigeons to books.

11. Answer: simile
Explanation: A simile is a comparison that usually uses the words like or as. The writer compares himself to a cloud in this sentence.

12. Answer: personification
Explanation: Personification gives human qualities to something that is non-human. Stars are given human qualities in this sentence.

13. Answer: B
Explanation: A connotation is an idea or feeling associated with a word. The word *sprightly* has a positive connotation in this sentence.

14. Answer: D
Explanation: The word *excruciating* means painful in the context of the text.

15. Answer: C
Explanation: The word *promising* means "likely to succeed" in the context of this text.

16. Answer: B
Explanation: A connotation is an idea or feeling associated with a word. The phrase "felt like an eternity" has a negative connotation in this sentence.

17. Answer: B
Explanation: This statement is false. Figurative language is a figure a speech and is not used to make literal comparisons in a text.

18. Answer: A
Explanation: This statement is true. Connotation refers to a feeling or idea associated with a word.

19. Answer: B
Explanation: This statement is false. Denotation is not a type of figurative language. Denotation refers to the literal meaning of a word.

20. Answer: A
Explanation: This statement is true. The word hyperactive refers to extreme activity.

4.2. Chapter Review

1. Answer: D
Explanation: The word *tormentors* mean bullies in the context of this text.

2. Answer: A
Explanation: The phrase "they were evil-looking creatures" indicates that Buck thought the men wanted to harm him.

prepaze

ANSWER KEY

3. Answer: C
Explanation: The word *deposited* means to be placed or put down in the context of this text.

4. Answer: B
Explanation: The word *deserted* means empty in the context of this text.

5. Answer: C
Explanation: The phrase "since everyone was at sports" indicates that there were no people in the area.

6. Answer: A
Explanation: A connotation is an idea or feeling associated with a word. The word capacious has a positive connotation in this sentence.

7. Answer: Answers will vary
Explanation: Students should be able to identify word meanings/connotations based on context clues. In this text, the author uses other adjectives such as handsome and impressive to describe the scenery. It can be inferred that the word *capacious* is similar in its meaning and connotation.

8. Answer: A
Explanation: This phrase means that she had finally come home after a long wait.

9. Answer: A
Explanation: This statement is true. The use of the word "poor" refers to the family's socioeconomic status.

10. Answer: B
Explanation: This statement is false. The phrase "learn his lessons at the same time" refers to Little Tuk trying to study his geography lesson while caring for his sister.

11. Answer: B
Explanation: This phrase means that he is dressed admirably.

12. Answer: B
Explanation: The word *inhabitants* refer to people who live in a certain place in this text.

13. Answer: C
Explanation: The word *sun-kissed* means warm in the context of this text.

14. Answer: B
Explanation: The word *interlacing* means tangled in the context of this text.

15. Answer: A
Explanation: The word *array* means an arrangement in the context of this text.

16. Answer: D
Explanation: The word *plunge* refers to an act of jumping or diving quickly in the context of this text.

17. Answer: B
Explanation: The word *prominent* means well-known in the context of this text.

18. Answer: B
Explanation: The word *adequately* means properly in the context of this text.

19. Answer: C
Explanation: The word *transgression* means violation in the context of this text.

20. Answer: D
Explanation: The word disgrace means shame in the context of this text.

21. Answer: C
Explanation: The phrase "a brass band's worth of greeting" most likely means that the birds sang loudly like a brass band playing instruments.

ANSWER KEY

22. Answer: D
Explanation: The phrase "mist lay on the surface of the water" most likely means that there were drops of mist on top of the water.

23. Answer: A
Explanation: The word *eagerly* means excitedly in the context of this text.

24. Answer: D
Explanation: The phrase "He broke his fall by grasping the golden pole" means that he stopped himself from falling by grasping the pole.

25. Answer: A
Explanation: An idiom is a figure of speech that uses words to express something other than the literal meaning. This phrase uses the words "broke his fall" to express the act of stopping.

26. Answer: D
Explanation: The phrase "He slowed as if a wind had sprung up from nowhere" means that he slowed down suddenly.

27. Answer: C
Explanation: A simile is a comparison that usually uses the words *like or as*. This phrase compares the act of slowing down to a wind.

28. Answer: B
Explanation: This phrase means that a few small raindrops continued to fall.

29. Answer: D
Explanation: This phrase means that Gatsby is staring blankly with little expression.

30. Answer: A
Explanation: The word bleared means dimmed or blurred in the context of this text.

END OF YEAR ASSESSMENT

1. Answer: B
Explanation: This statement is false. The interaction between the subjects of the poem does not create a sense of humor in the text.

2. Answer: A
Explanation: This statement is true. Th Booker T.'s perspective is less assertive than W.E.B's point of view.

3. Answer: A
Explanation: The poem is an argument between two points of view on civil rights.

4. Answer: A
Explanation: The scientist realizes that he is responsible for Frankenstein's creation and actions.

5. Answer: B
Explanation: This quote demonstrates the realization of the scientist that he is Frankenstein's creator, and is responsible for him.

6. Answer: D
Explanation: It angers him that Shere Khan is breaking the rules of the jungle.

7. Answer: D
Explanation: All of these lines demonstrate how Tabaqui is trying to cause trouble with Father and Mother Wolf.

8. Answer: C
Explanation: The second text refers to characters from the first text.

9. Answer: B
Explanation: Both texts are written in a narrative style.

ANSWER KEY

10.   Answer: C

Explanation: The central idea of the passage is that airplanes are the best way to travel overseas.

11.   Answer: A

Explanation: The sentence "Although boating is a feasible option, flying is the quickest route." best supports the central idea of the passage.

12.   Answer: C

Explanation: The sentence "Airplanes are bad for the environment" does not support the central idea of the passage.

13.   Answer: A

Explanation: The sentence "Flying is the quickest and most cost-efficient way to travel overseas" also summarizes the central idea of the passage.

14.   Answer: A

Explanation: This statement is true. The author's purpose is to inform the reader about proper baking techniques.

15.   Answer: B

Explanation: This statement is false. The term "spoiled" refers to ruining the cake.

16.   Answer: D

Explanation: The text is structured in a descriptive style, offering precise details about baking a cake.

17.   Answer: C

Explanation: The article says, "Norway is well known for its amazing and varied scenery."

18.   Answer: B

Explanation: Norway is the most northern of the Scandinavian countries. The name for the aurora borealis is "northern lights." Students should make the connection between those two facts.

19.   Answer: A

Explanation: Nearly everything in the text relates specifically to Sweden.

20.   Answer: B

Explanation: The previous article deals only with Norway, so the correct answer for this question must also. Choice B is the only answer that specifically mentions Norway.

21.   Answer: A

Explanation: According to the text, Sweden prides itself on its outdoors and natural beauty, more so than the need to be more populous.

22.   Answer: D

Explanation: Even though the text mentions cities, parks, and mountains, the areas in which people are not allowed are not specified. They could be pristine, dangerous, classified by the government, etc.

23.   Answer: D

Explanation: Nearly everything the author of the article discusses points to how wasteful drinking bottled water is.

24.   Answer: B

Explanation: There are many statistics that back up the author's main claim in the article, from how many bottles are discarded to the amount of fuel it takes to make one bottle.

25.   Answer: C

Explanation: The result of a research study about the environmental effects of bottled water is an example of relevant evidence.

26.   Answer: A

Explanation: The role Columbus's father-in-law played in his life is only emphasized in the first source..

ANSWER KEY

27. Answer: Answers will vary

Explanation: Students should be able to explain how two texts about the same topic can present information in different ways. Ex.: The second passage displays Columbus as an individual who accomplished his tasks on his own, while the other source emphasizes the support he received from his father-in-law.

28. Answer: C

Explanation: In order to best illustrate the physical details of the artwork, photos would be the best medium.

29. Answer: C

Explanation: This statement is not true. Print books can be just as reliable as digital tools.

30. Answer: A

Explanation: The sentence, "Some people assert that dogs do not need to be on a flea preventative medicine" is a counterclaim that opposes the author's argument.

31. Answer: D

Explanation: All of these statements could be used to support this topic.

32. Answer: B

Explanation: One of the purposes of a story's introduction is to introduce the characters

33. Answer: A

Explanation: The student is not writing about the task that the teacher assigned.

34. Answer: D

Explanation: The final draft is the last step in the writing process after edits and revisions have been completed so is a close as possible to error-free.

35. Answer: B

Explanation: This statement is false. An old resource can still contain accurate information.

36. Answer: A

Explanation: This statement is true. Transition words such as "furthermore" and "in addition to" can help to develop your essay topic.

37. Answer: B

Explanation: This statement is false. The writing process should be followed for all types of formal writing.

38. Answer: A

Explanation: This statement is true. An audience should be considered for each writing piece.

39. Answer: Answers will vary

Explanation: Students should be able to write a personal narrative using proper techniques.

40. Answer: B

Explanation: The word *marred* means blemished in the context of this text.

41. Answer: C

Explanation: This phrase means that the narrator lost her excitement about having a book.

42. Answer: A

Explanation: The word audible means "easily heard" in the context of this text.

43. Answer: C

Explanation: The word *resiliency* means strength in the context of this text.

44. Answer: C

Explanation: This phrase most likely means that the dust began to dissolve in the rain.

45. Answer: B

Explanation: The word *emitted* means released in the context of this text.

END OF YEAR ASSESSMENT

REFERENCES CITED

- *"Cinderella"* By Charles Perrault (Adapted)

- *15 Epic Reasons to Visit Chicago* From Choosechicago.com

- *Countries of the World: Norway* By National Geographic Kids

- Excerpt *"Little Tuk"* from Fairy Tales Written by Hans Christian Andersen

- Excerpt adapted from *"The Necklace"* By Guy de Maupassant

- Excerpt adapted from *Oliver Twist* By Charles Dickens

- Excerpt adapted from *The Logic of Vegetarianism* By Henry S. Salt

- Excerpt adapted from *The White House Cookbook* By F.L. Gillette

- Excerpt from *"Annabel Lee"* By Edgar Allan Poe

- Excerpt from *"Booker T. and W.E.B."* By Randall DuBois

- Excerpt from *"Caged Bird"* By Maya Angelou

- Excerpt from *"Gift of the Magi"* Written by O. Henry

- Excerpt from *"I Wandered Lonely as a Cloud"* By William Wordsworth

- Excerpt from *"Mending Wall"* By Robert Frost

- Excerpt from *"Rapunzel"* From the Brothers Grimm Version

- Excerpt from *"The Raven"* By Edgar Allen Poe

- Excerpt from *"The Tell-Tale Heart"* Written by Edgar Allan Poe

- Excerpt from *A Separate Peace* Written by John Knowles

- Excerpt from *American Leaders and Heroes* Written by Wilbur F. Gordy

- Excerpt from *Black Beauty: The Autobiography of a Horse* Written by Anna Sewell

- Excerpt from *Dorothy Payne, Quakeress: A Side-Light upon the Career of 'Dolly' Madison* Written by Ella Kent Barnard

- Excerpt from *Fahrenheit 451* Written by Ray Bradbury

REFERENCES CITED

- Excerpt from *Frankenstein* Written by Mary Shelley

- Excerpt from *Great Expectations* Written by Charles Dickinson

- Excerpt from *Lord of the Flies* Written by William Golding

- Excerpt from *Much Ado About Nothing* By William Shakespeare, adapted by Farrar Williams

- Excerpt from *Roll of Thunder, Hear My Cry* Written by Mildred Taylor

- Excerpt from *Romeo and Juliet* Act II, Scene II by William Shakespeare

- https://www.copyrightfreecontent.com/newsusa/hazards-that-are-most-likely-to-hurt-your-tires/

- https://www.copyrightfreecontent.com/technology/the-smart-home-and-our-connected-life-2/

- Excerpt from the article *"Turn on the Taps! Bottled Water Industry is Bad for the Earth"* By Project Syndicate

- https://fairuse.stanford.edu/overview/public-domain/welcome/

- Excerpt from http://www.gutenberg.org/cache/epub/60718/pg60718.txt

- Excerpt from *The Call of the Wild* Written by Jack London

- Excerpt from the fable *"Two Brothers"* By Aesop

- Excerpt from *The Great Gatsby* Written by F. Scott Fitzgerald

- Excerpt from *The Invisible Library* Written by Genevieve Cogman

- Excerpt from *The Jungle Book* Written by Rudyard Kipling

REFERENCES CITED

- Excerpt from *The Life of Christopher Columbus* Written by Edward Everett Hale

- Excerpt from *Tuck Everlasting* Written by Natalie Babbitt

- *Shall I Compare Thee To A Summer's Day?* by William Shakespeare (Sonnet 18)

- *The Daisy* Written by Hans Christian Andersen

- *The Fox and the Horse* Written by Jacob and Wilhelm Grimm

- *The New Colossus* by Emma Lazarus

- *To Dorothy* By Marvin Bell

- https://www.copyrightfreecontent.com/newsusa/michelin-tires-helps-yellowstone-national-park-go-green/

- https://www.copyrightfreecontent.com/arts-and-entertainment/mickey-mouse-of-japan-goes-stateside/

- https://publicdomainreview.org/essay/greenland-unicorns-and-the-magical-alicorn

- Adapted from https://en.wikipedia.org/wiki/Eunice_Newton_Foote

Made in the USA
Columbia, SC
13 December 2022